LFA T'AI C

C000132794

Chang Ming
T'ai Chi Long Life Diet
and Recipe Book

By Sheila Dickinson
President of the LFA Health Arts

T'ai Chi Guide and Recipe Book for Healthy
Living

Printed and published in Great Britain by

STAIRWAY
DISTRIBUTION
LTD.

P O BOX 19,
HEDON,
HULL
HU12 8YR

First Published 2003

Published by Stairway Distribution Limited
PO Box 19, Hedon. Hull. HU12 8YR
www.leefamilyarts.com

Please consult your Doctor before taking part in the following
exercise programme.
The LFA and Stairway Distribution Ltd disclaim any liability
for loss or injury in connection with the advice and exercises
included in this book.

Acknowledgements

To the past Masters of our Arts - we offer our sincere thanks!

I would also like to extend my heartfelt thanks to my good friends Diane Ward, Olive Richardson, Sheena Judge and Beryl Hunter for donating their healthy recipes and for their friendship.

Cover Design by Karl Robinson
(a very talented Artist and Graphics Designer) It gives me great pleasure to append his email address for others to contact him (karlrobinson@hotmail.com) and enjoy his artistic creations.

Books by the same author:-

T'AI CHI FORM   (MOVEMENTS 1 TO 140)
T'AI CHI DANCE   (MOVEMENTS 1 TO 184)
T'AI CHI STICK   (MOVEMENTS 1 TO 150)
T'AI CHI SILK   (MOVEMENTS 1 TO 156)
T'AI CHI SWORD   (MOVEMENTS 1 TO 108)
T'AI CHI NUNCHAKU (MOVEMENTS 1 TO 150)
T'AI CHI FAN   (MOVEMENTS 1 TO 150)
CHANG MING T'AI CHI LONG LIFE DIET AND RECIPE BOOK

VIDEOS by the same author:-

T'AI CHI FORM   (MOVEMENTS 1 TO 50)
T'AI CHI DANCE   (MOVEMENTS 1 TO 50)
T'AI CHI STICK   (MOVEMENTS 1 TO 50)
T'AI CHI SILK   (MOVEMENTS 1 TO 50)
T'AI CHI SWORD   (MOVEMENTS 1 TO 50)

Available from: -

Stairway Distribution Limited
P O Box 19
Hedon
Hull
HU12 8YR
Tel / Fax 01482 896063

Or visit our Website www.leefamilyarts.com

CHANG MING

THE LFA T'AI CHI LIBRARY

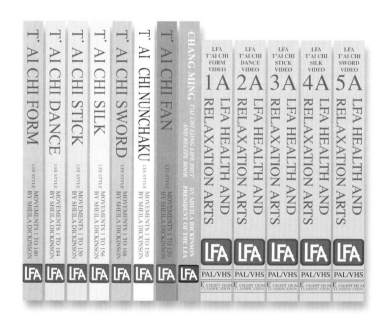

All of the above Books and Videos are available from:-
Stairway Distribution Limited
PO Box 19
Hedon
HU12 8YR
Tel/Fax 01482 896063

You may also order from our Website catalogue, please visit
www.leefamilyarts.com

CONTENTS

Important

Please turn to pages 177 and 178 to find out why the Chang Ming Diet is vital to your health.

Foreword

Welcome to the Lee Family Arts Chang Ming T'ai Chi Long Life Diet and Recipe book. Please note, I have extended the foreword in this book in order that I can firstly pay tribute to my late Grand Master Chee Soo and secondly draw your attention to some of the important information on the diet and the structure of this book.

My position as President of the Lee Family Arts started in January 1995. Since that time, I have had the privilege to guide my fellow instructors in all aspects of LFA T'ai Chi, and I have worked hard to reach as many people as possible, so that everyone may gain from the many health benefits of our Arts.

I would not be writing this book today without the guidance and patience of my late Grand Master Chee Soo, who spent most of his life teaching the Lee Family Arts. Chee Soo is in my thoughts constantly and I offer my sincere thanks for receiving the benefit of his wisdom and understanding.

Chee Soo wrote five books published by the Aquarian Press, sadly at the time of writing only one title remains in print today 'The Chinese Art of T'ai Chi Ch'uan'. In this book he traces the history of the Lee Style back to Ho-Hsieh Lee circa 1,000BC. It is stated that the Lee Family have always been Taoists and that the Lee Style is a Yin and Yang style, this means that everything within it is in complete balance and harmony.

Chee Soo occasionally spoke of his own Grand Master, Chan Kam Lee and told of how they had met during 1934 in Hyde Park in London. In those days there were very few Oriental people in London and the two became friends. It was a friendship that would change Chee Soo's life forever. After Chan Kam Lee's death, Chee Soo dedicated himself to maintaining the knowledge and wisdom he had learnt from Chan Kam Lee.

While staying with my family and my self, Chee Soo talked to me about the future of the Lee Family Arts and the direction he wished them to take. On Monday the 16th May 1994 Chee Soo asked me to give him my word that I would not let the Lee Family Arts die. Sadly Chee Soo died on the 29th August 1994.

It is with the greatest respect to Chee Soo that I offer my own writings and understanding of the lessons he taught me.

The names of Instructors who have trained, qualified and still maintain their own training can be obtained from the Lee Family Arts official register of qualified instructors. The LFA can only vouch for the quality and content of that which is taught within an official LFA registered class. The Lee Family Arts have been tried and tested for thousands of years before we were born. The people who teach them are merely caretakers, who have the privilege of maintaining the Arts, and witnessing them helping others.

This book not only teaches you that eating the correct food can enhance the quality of your life, it also gives information on feeling good, losing weight, yin and yang, skin tones, all of the LFA T'ai Chi sets and living the Taoist way. My aim was to produce a book which draws together all the elements of our Arts, and show that the Chang Ming diet is an integral part of learning and living LFA T'ai Chi.

The Lee Family Arts will always be known as a Family Art and it is a family that grows in numbers daily. In concluding, I would like to say a very special welcome to you!

It is important that you now read pages 177 and 178 in order that you fully understand the essence of the Chang Ming Diet.

Feel Good Factor

The only qualification you need to learn LFA T'ai Chi is to be able to smile. Take the first step today and embrace the feel good factor which awaits you.

I was recently asked to define LFA T'ai Chi and what exactly makes it so special? One's first instinct is to try and justify why the Lee Family Arts are so good and why everyone should practise them. The best answer is that the Lee Family Arts 'just is'.

From your very first class you will start to learn the basic mechanics, a smile will cross your face and although you might not realise it straight away, you have taken your very first step on a special journey.

LFA T'ai Chi does not possess a magic wand, although some of our results sometimes appear spectacular. The movements work subtly and we do not always recognise the changes which are taking place within ourselves. Often it is our friends, family or colleagues who first notice the changes. LFA students have more energy, a greater enthusiasm for life - approaching it with a far more laid back attitude. There are many styles of T'ai Chi in the world and their practitioners will eagerly state that their style is equally as good as the others, if not the best. It is not my aim to argue my case but simply to state that both as a student, then as an instructor and latterly as President of the LFA, I have witnessed our style help many people. I heartily recommend LFA T'ai Chi, purely and simply, because it works.

Many people claim to have studied T'ai Chi for twenty or thirty years and consider themselves to be an expert on the subject. I recently met one such person. In reality from that one meeting, I knew that they had given their time to learning the physical movements, (which were gracefully performed). Sadly, they had never progressed past the physical side, and never found any of the many layers within T'ai Chi which were waiting to be discovered.

The whole of the LFA Lee Family Arts is based upon teaching you how to harness, store and utilise natural energies and we do this in a caring, professional way because we are here to help you feel better both internally and externally.

Internal Energy (Chi)

Your chi energy is with you from the day you are born until the day you die. From about the age of five or six we allow our physical energy to take over and our chi energy lies dormant.

Very few of us have any understanding of what our chi energy is capable of until we start practising LFA T'ai Chi, yet it is so vital to the good health of our mind, body and spirit.

A person with a highly developed chi will experience very few illnesses, even the common cold will become a thing of the past.

It is my job to show you how to activate your internal energy. Although I can act as a guide, it is up to you to provide the dedication and practice to achieve this. There are no short cuts and everyone has to pass through each of the stages. My late master, Chee Soo, once said to me "everyone wants to be at the top of the mountain, but everyone wants to take a lift." We are all aware that there is no lift and it is up to each of us to make the climb. Only when you have passed through all the stages can you benefit from constant good health and peace of mind.

T'ai Chi Long Life Diet

People view growing old as acceptance of aches, pains, memory loss etc - this should not be the case. If you pass through all the various stages of your training, age will bring knowledge and experience. Old age then holds promises of the joys which come from the experience of 'living life' and truly experiencing 'good health'.

One of the first stages when developing your chi energy is to learn how to completely relax your mind, body and spirit. This is where the movements of our T'ai Chi Form begin to come into play.

At first you will be too busy thinking about where your hands and feet should be rather than worrying about any problems which you may have. Eventually, as the movements become second nature to you, peace will descend upon you, this is because the movements work the channels within your body which move your chi energy. Physically, all the joints are kept mobile without strain, and the specialised breathing patterns will help to expel toxins from your body.
To many people, relaxation means flopping into an armchair, - this is one of the worst things you can do as it makes your mind and body become lazy.

Furthermore you will find it harder to show enthusiasm for life. If you feel really tired, try practising one of our many breathing exercises, it will only take a few minutes and could well give you the lift you need. People who are truly interested in developing and storing their chi energy should start to incorporate specialised breathing exercises and our Chang Ming diet into their daily routine.

When you have developed your chi energy, the next stage is to learn how to move it around your body from its storehouse in your lower abdomen (Tan T'ien)....

Like flicking a switch on, your chi energy will flow along the channels housed in your bones, muscles and tissues throughout the whole of your body. At this stage, there are specialised breathing exercises which are taught to help you gain complete mastery of yourself thus allowing your chi energy to be moved without any physical strength. Your Tan T'ien has a limited capacity and once you start to develop your chi energy, it will overflow into your pelvic area, from here it is moved to benefit the whole of your mind, body and spirit. The movement of your chi energy will give your body greater strength and flexibility. If however, you adopt poor eating habits, this could well restrict the flow of your chi and in turn affect your health. That is why someone who is truly interested in obtaining good health should follow the **Chang Ming** diet.

The Chang Ming diet was converted for the Western way of life by Grand Master Chan Kam Lee in the 1930's. At first sight it may seem like a difficult diet to follow, although those of us who do truly follow it know that like anything else, it becomes easier through time. In this book, I will explain the Chang Ming diet in greater detail and offer some easy to follow recipes.
One of the many benefits of the Chang Ming diet is that it prevents the intake of toxins into the body. This is because the food is in its most natural state and unrefined.

It takes roughly three years of eating the Chang Ming way before the body is considered to be healthy! That is why Chee Soo stated "prospective parents should be on the diet for at least three years before they have a baby; if they wish to give their children the best possible start in life". Furthermore, our bones are all sealed units and the heat of your chi energy is passed along the surface of the bones. Very slowly, over the passing of time, the bone itself becomes heated and this in turn will heat the marrow. That is why very dedicated practitioners of our Arts will not suffer from bone marrow diseases. It takes 10 years for the diet to have the full beneficial effect on the bones

It is important to point out that you also have to watch for other substances which we readily take in without much thought of their long term affects on our bodies. Chee Soo used to warn that it takes the body six months to rid itself of the effects of taking one aspirin. However, over the years I have personally found that through practising our T'ai Chi forms and the many specialised breathing exercises, in conjunction with the Chang Ming diet, my body is well able to cope without resorting to the use of pills.

External Energy (Li)

Li energy is very important to us as it supports the planets in the universe. This energy is everywhere and is passing through you even as you read this book. Li energy comes from the heavens passing through all things yang (male) on its downward journey. It then enters the earth, turns 180 degrees and passes through all things yin (female) on its upward journey. The ancient sages of China are said to have used this energy to live to 150 or 200 years of age.

Li energy gives life and vitality to all plants - if you are feeling ill and sit underneath a tree you will perhaps find that you feel a little better. This is because, even in your weakened state, you are drawing li energy from the tree.

In LFA T'ai Chi, we teach you to harness li energy and couple this with your internal energy, chi. People at an advanced stage of their personal development, may find it possible to use this external energy for healing - this is achieved through advanced mind control.
If you are interested in the development of this energy

you should also study the ancient art of K'ai Men. These exercises are taught within all of our classes. K'ai Men means 'open door'. Chee Soo stated "the Taoists have known for thousands of years that cancer is due to very low internal and external energies and it is everyones responsibility to build up these energies". Healing with energy does not require any special equipment, just a sound knowledge of how the energies work and how they move around the body.

In the western world we tend to rely on our GPs to give us relief from our ailments. I am not, for one moment, suggesting that you should no longer visit them, what I am suggesting works in conjunction with Western medicine. We have choices, I personally have not visited a doctor for over twenty years. This does not mean that I never experience the odd cold, but I choose to treat this by applying an **onion poultice**:

T'ai Chi Healing Techniques

ONION POULTICE
Components: -
a neck scarf
1 onion (about the size of a large egg peeled and

finely chopped)
Place the chopped, raw onion in the scarf, fold the scarf over to enclose the onion, and wear the scarf around your neck with the onion poultice underneath your chin. Change the onion poultice every 6 hours and wear them for 24-36 until the cold / influenza has been broken. I find that if I apply an onion poultice as soon as I feel the slightest flu like symptoms, they do not develop any further. However, most people would rather suffer the effects of flu than risk the smell of the onions, but you could choose to wear it at night! Any odour will wash off.

I have also found an onion compress excellent for the relief of a stiff neck, ear ache and sore throats.

Chee Soo also stated in his book, the Tao of Long Life, "an onion poultice applied to the area of the kidneys would help to stimulate them and if applied the calves of the legs it can help to relieve heart trouble".

The versatile onion may also be heated and placed between two cloths and placed on areas of the body which have poor circulation.

Another excellent remedy I have found for **congested sinuses** is **ginger steam**. Below is a list of some of the ways in which I recommend using ginger:

GINGER STEAM (ground spice)
Required: -
1 bowl
1 towel
Half a small tub of ginger spice
Boiling water
(BE CAREFUL NOT TO SCALD YOURSELF).
Place the half tub of ground ginger spice in a bowl of boiling water. Lower your head over the bowl, cover it over with the towel and inhale the steam.

GINGER BATH (ground ginger)
Ginger spice can also be used in a hot bath to relieve aching joints. People suffering from arthritis have told me that they have experienced great relief from taking a ginger bath before going to bed. People who suffer from insomnia have also experienced a good night's sleep after sitting in a ginger bath.
Your bath water should be as hot as you are able to stand it and the water should be no higher than your navel. Place a towel around your shoulders to keep the upper part of your body warm. If you are able to sit in the bath for a period of fifteen minutes you will receive the greatest benefits.

GINGER TEA (root ginger)
Required: -
1 pan
Grated ginger root (2oz)
2pts water
Place the ginger and water into the pan and bring the water to the boil. Turn the heat down and simmer for 10 minutes. Strain and drink a cupful at a time. If you wish you can add a little honey.
This is very good for the relief of sore throats and coughs.

GINGER COMPRESS
(root ginger or ground ginger)
WARNING: A GINGER COMPRESS SHOULD NOT BE APPLIED TO THE NECK OR HEART AREA.

Required: -
2oz grated root ginger
2pts boiling water
1 pan
1 pair of rubber gloves
1 dolly bag (or the end of a clean stocking)
2 face cloths

Place the grated ginger root in the dolly bag and add it to the pan of boiling water. Lower the heat and simmer for 15 minutes. Place one of the face cloths into the simmering liquid.

Wearing the rubber gloves, wring out the cloth as tightly as possible and apply to the area of pain. Place the second cloth into the pan. As soon as the first face cloth cools, return it to the pan and prepare and apply the second hot cloth. Repeat for a period of 15 minutes. Depending upon where the area of pain is, you may need someone to help you to apply the cloths.

You can use the same liquid over and over again.
I personally have found that a ginger compress is excellent for relieving back pain. When I first started studying T'ai Chi, I had to have a ginger compress applied to my back every day for a whole year, however, I no longer suffer from back pain thanks to the ginger compress and LFA T'ai Chi!

SAGE
WARNING - NURSING MOTHERS SHOULD NOT DRINK SAGE TEA

Sage is an excellent herb to use as a tea. The benefits

can be tremendous i.e.
- Calming the mind
- Increasing the appetite
- Helping menstruation (ensuring it is regular)
- Helping the kidneys
- Helping the liver

Infuse a pinch of dried sage in boiling water, strain when ready to drink (honey may be added to taste)

PARSLEY

Parsley is another excellent herb that may be used as a tea and is very beneficial to your well being and strengthening the kidneys. I have been taught that the kidneys are the most important organs in the body, with this in mind, I drink parsley tea on a regular basis.

Infuse a pinch of dried parsley in boiling water, strain when ready to drink (honey may be added to taste).

TARRAGON

Tarragon makes an excellent tea which can help the heart, liver and brain plus strengthen the memory. This herb has a rather strong taste and **should not be used with other herbs**.

FENNEL
This is an excellent herb and can be used as a vegetable or tea. Fennel is good for breaking up phlegm; it also helps to get rid of surplus fat furthermore it helps milk production in nursing mothers and eases intestinal pain.

DATES
Dates make an excellent tonic against fatigue. Simply simmer the flesh and stones together in a small amount of water until a thick liquid appears. Drain and drink the liquid in dessert spoonfuls. This can also be effective for combating a weak stomach, low energy levels and anaemia. (You can use the left over flesh as a filling for a wholemeal pastry pie after removing the stones.)

CABBAGE POULTICE
I have personally found the cabbage poultice an excellent way of reducing swelling and have used it successfully when treating friends.

Take the clean large leaves of a cabbage; remove the stem then iron on both sides until the cabbage leaf is hot and smooth. Next apply it to the area of pain and

T'ai Chi Long Life Diet

hold it in place with a bandage. Go to bed with the bandage on and allow the cabbage to do its work. Remove the poultice the next morning. It is also said to ease bruising and pain from knocks, although, I have always found the ginger compress very successful for easing pain.

CHINESE TEA
Green tea and black tea are both used to help to fight colds, relieve headaches, benefit the circulation of the chi energy. They can also help to strengthen weak eyes.

In this day and age, many western world drugs come with warnings of possible side effects, yet how many people do you know who take a pill to cure an ailment and then take another one to correct the side effects of the first pill. In the LFA we work with western medicine and are offering an additional way that can help to eliminate a lot of the aches and pains which many people experience in every day life, without any negative side effects.
Please consult your doctor if you have any doubts about the above. There is no reason why Eastern and Western medicine should not work together.

Losing Weight The LFA Way

Are you overweight? Have you tried to follow a diet only to put more weight back on afterwards?

Only one person controls what you put into your mouth and eat and that is **you**. Have you ever eaten something you really didn't want to just to please others?

Now the big question - do you over eat? If the answer is yes, then the next question has to be 'why'?

Having a truly healthy body is about more than following the latest fad in diets. True good health comes from a healthier way of life.

In the western world we have the luxury of eating for pleasure, yet in other parts of the world people starve. Some of us eat because we are bored, yet how can we be bored, when, more than ever before, there are so many things to fill up our time?

If you are overweight, then quite simply, something is out of balance, and it is up to you to do something about it. No one can do it for you. Eating an extra treat may make you feel better while you are eating it, however, the effect usually lasts for the same amount of time as it took to eat the chocolate bar.

LFA T'ai Chi is interested in curing a problem at its root. If you are feeling lonely, unhappy or stressed, a chocolate bar may taste good but it certainly won't solve the problem. You have to feel good about yourself, and a true feeling of greater well-being comes from within. Only you can start the process - only you can improve the quality of your life.

If I asked you who is the most important person in your world, I wonder what your answer would be. Do you know that **you** are the most important person? You have it within your own power to find and develop a better way of living and in doing so, you are able to help everyone who comes into contact with you. Remember, the Chang Ming diet is not some latest fad; it is over 3000 years old and works by balancing and harmonising the body from the inside.

The Chang Ming diet was first written about in Chee Soo's book 'The Tao of Long Life'. He explained that Chan Kam Lee translated the diet into English so that we in the west could reap the benefits. It is not specifically a slimming diet although your body will come to settle at its natural weight. Chang Ming is all about improving your health.

I have heard hundreds of reasons why people do not adopt the Chang Ming diet. We have choices and the price we pay for being frivolous belongs to ourselves. Should we wait until problems become apparent or take action which avoids the problem occurring.

If you are used to buying take-a-ways and relying on convenience foods, then you are filling your body with the wrong types of food and not only can you become over weight by following these eating patterns, you can also damage your health. Carrying extra weight can place a strain on all of the organs of the body. The knock on effect is that your natural energy levels can drop and although you might be able to cope today, the question which has to be asked is "what about tomorrow"?

With the advancement of modern science, people are living to a far greater age than ever before, however, it is our individual responsibility to keep our mind and body in good working order. Every one of us has the responsibility to maintain our own good health until the day we die. Damaging our minds and bodies by eating and drinking in an unhealthy way and then saying 'doctor, doctor, save me' is not an adult option. After all, it is not only the individual who pays the price for over indulgence, but also the people who love and care about them. The thought of ever being a burden to my family or friends is something I would not like to contribute to.

In the LFA, we suggest you follow the Chang Ming diet and we can offer you special guidance when trying to lose weight. For example,

Start by trying to keep to eating only three meals a day

The ancient Taoists found that eating only twice a day ensured the body had sufficient time to rest between each meal. This made sure the body received the maximum amount of nourishment from the food.

A excellent and easy tip, not only for people who are trying to lose weight, is to purchase a non stick wok or large frying pan. Try the following nourishing meal.

- Place chopped mushrooms and chopped onions into the pan.

- Add finely chopped vegetables of your choice.
- Cover the pan with a lid and cook the vegetables on a low heat
- Add some soy sauce (instead of salt) to season

You are able to eat as many vegetables and salads as you like without putting on weight.

Some other useful tips:
- If you eat meat, use grilled chicken or fish
- Try not to use too much oil when cooking
- For dessert, try a chopped banana in natural yoghurt, or eat an apple
- Reduce the size of your portions
- Apply common sense to your eating habits

It is also important that you do not under eat. There is no reason why your plate should not be full, as long as you take a sensible approach regarding what is on your plate.

A desert invented by my husband is to dice an apple and a banana into a small dish, then mix some oats and honey together. Spread the oats and honey mixture over the top of the chopped fruit and bake in the oven until golden brown.

This makes a desert that is low in fat, yet the oats provide a high energy giving food, and honey is also one of nature's natural antiseptics.

If you are used to picking at tip bits, for example while you are working at your computer or watching the television, then the problem is more to do with the mind than with the fact that you are hungry. This is where LFA T'ai Chi comes into its own. Instead of reaching for an edible source of comfort practise one of our breathing exercises. Your mind will eventually be able to control the craving.

There are people who have to eat regularly because of certain health problems and I suggest a healthy option instead of preservative packed food.

In the early stages of changing your eating habits, your mind will keep suggesting that you need more food. However, unless it has been medically suggested for health reasons, this is not usually the case. Try one of our easy breathing exercise instead.

A sensible approach is required when planning your meals and it is best to plan in advance. If you wait until you walk through the door from work, the temptation to order a take-away may prove too great.

Within the K'ai Men element of our health arts, we have exercises designed to tone every part of the body (see the LFA T'ai Chi K'ai Men Book). I strongly recommend practising these exercises in conjunction with the Chang Ming diet, although remember, as with all of our exercises there **should be no strain**.

Practising our T'ai Chi Dance, Stick or Silk will provide you with a cardio-vascular workout. The different disciplines within our Arts compliment each other, helping each person to find complete harmony between mind, body and spirit.

The T'ai Chi Silk is especially beneficial if you are trying to lose weight and should be practised continually for twenty minutes three times per week. It is important that the arms form large circular movements, this will ensure that you gain the maximum benefit from our Silk set.

Anyone attending my day courses and workshops has the added advantage of being able to ask for a weekly diet sheet and toning exercises to help them achieve their desired goal of a slimmer, healthier body. Local LFA instructors are also available to help you.

Ladies, are you Yin or Yang?

Although this section is written especially with ladies in mind, all men should also be aware of how a balance of yin and yang can affect their partner.

I think most ladies would agree with me that menstruation is something we endure. In some cases our monthly cycles can mean erratic emotions, stomach cramps etc.

If you are **yin**, you will menstruate between the new moon and the full moon. You may experience irregular, long periods which leave you feeling weak and listless. At times, there might be excessive flow combined with stomach cramps. This can be caused by poor eating habits. If left unchecked, this in turn can lead to poor circulation.

It is best that your hair is left unwashed during this period to avoid taking extra dampness into your system. You should also avoid cold showers and baths. When a bath or shower is required it should be a quick, warm one.

In my early days of training I found I suffered from

severe stomach cramps each month. A ginger hipbath is an excellent way to overcome stomach cramps and help to stimulate your circulation. The ginger hipbath and the ginger compress are also excellent for breaking up fat deposits and dispersing cysts. Twice a year I have a ginger hipbath every night, for a week, as I feel this a kind of spring clean which ensures my body stays healthy. However if you suffer from a heavy vaginal discharge this can be due to excess fat deposits inside the vagina and I would strongly suggest you change your diet and take ginger hipbaths immediately.

This information is not offered instead of Western medicine, it is offered merely as preventative. Every lady should listen to her own body and act accordingly. The colour of the discharge may vary from white, yellow or green and this is a very important indicator of your internal health. These colours indicate a yin presence. If you wish to take action before it becomes something more serious, change your diet. A green discharge over a long period should be taken very seriously, if it is left untreated, cancer could form.

If you are **yang** you will menstruate at the time of the

full moon, you will find that your periods only last about three days and will appear at a regular twenty eight day intervals. This in turn will mean that your energy loss is much less than a yin lady. However, if you menstruate at intervals less than twenty eight days and experience thick heavy blood loss this means you are too yang and need to cut down on yang foods.

Pregnancy
A lady who is very yin is more likely to experience miscarriages and premature births. Long agonising births are also a sign of being yin. The feelings that a 'mum to be' experiences during her pregnancy will be passed on to her baby. It is the responsibility of not only the mother, but also the father to ensure that the mum has a carefree pregnancy and produces a happy contented baby.

If you are thinking of having a baby, please remember the information that my late master passed on to me. 'It takes two and a half years to grow one layer of skin tissue, so if you want your own and your baby's blood and tissue to be fully healthy, you should plan your pregnancy in advance'.

A yang mum-to-be will find that she carries her baby past the ninth month and into the tenth, this ensures her baby is provided with the best possible nourishment. When the time comes to give birth, a yang mum will find that labour is far easier when compared to a mum who is yin. With my first child, I was in labour for only three hours, although I wasn't practising the Lee Family Arts at that time. Looking back, I applied a lot of the principles associated with being yang without being aware of them.

Drinking fennel tea will help to ensure good milk production, this way you can give your baby the best possible start. I strongly emphasize the need to be wary of taking drugs while pregnant. We only need to look back in history to be reminded of some of the terrible side effects drugs can have on the unborn child.

For the first few days after childbirth, a fluid called colostrum comes from your breasts before your milk starts to flow. This liquid is very yang and will give your baby an added boost to help fight off bacteria and many diseases.

T'ai Chi Long Life Diet

Over the years I have taught many expectant mums'. All have been able to continue with their LFA classes for the full term of their pregnancy because the movements are practised without strain, thus making LFA T'ai Chi an ideal form of exercise to practise when pregnant. Within our Arts, we have exercises which are designed especially for the mum-to-be. Furthermore, an LFA instructor will always say if any exercise is not suitable and therefore should not be practised by anyone who thinks they may be pregnant.

If you would like exercises to practise during your pregnancy you can contact me by email at sheila@leefamilyarts.com or through your local instructor.

Remember you owe it to yourself and your unborn child to find out if you are yin or yang, then act accordingly.

Recognising Skin Tones

My late Master Chee Soo, taught how to recognise and understand the meanings behind different skin tones and explained them as follows.

A pale complexion is often commonplace in the western world. If white spots sometimes appear on the face or body this can indicate the intake of too much dairy produce. In turn, this causes a yin condition, often representing poor blood quality or anaemia. I am not saying everyone with a pale complexion should panic. However, a change in diet would go a long way towards creating a healthy complexion.

A **pale, glossy skin** can outwardly represent the signs of lung problems. I would strongly recommend practising our specialised breathing exercises.

Often, a **greying complexion** can indicate that a person has problems within the liver. Another symptom of this colour can be volatile emotions or bouts of depression. This colouring also represents a yin condition.

A **darkening of the skin** between brown and black

may indicate kidney problems. Parsley tea provides an excellent way of cleansing and nourishing the kidneys.

Yellow can indicate problems connected with the spleen, pancreas, liver, indicating jaundice. The intake of too much sugar into the body can greatly affect the function of the pancreas, once again emphasizing the importance of correct eating and drinking.

Red, although often associated with yang conditions, this can indicate poor circulation and blood stagnation therefore it is a yin condition. Chee Soo explained that if someone was suffering from a fever, that part of the face which turned red represented the organ which was under duress:

- A red **complexion** indicates the heart
- A red **nose** shows sickness of the spleen
- Red on the **left side of the jaw** points to the liver being under duress
- Red on the **right side of the jaw** signifies disease in the lungs
- A red **chin** could points to trouble in the kidneys

In all of the above, a very strong yin influence is indicated.

Pink (although normally associated with a healthy complexion), if a deep pink glow appears in the afternoon, along with sweaty palms, night sweats and a red tongue, this could indicate tuberculosis, which should be checked out by a doctor.

Blue/purple indicates too many toxins in the blood. Anyone with this colouring should go on a strict Chang Ming diet and cut out the cause.

Green is the colour to beware of as this could denote cancer. The left side of the face denotes the liver and the right side the lungs.

If you are truly healthy your skin should be a glowing pink throughout the year. Your skin should be warm to the touch whatever the weather.

A few other points to note about the skin are:
- Red skin colour in a new baby is perfectly healthy, for as it grows in strength the baby

becomes more yang.
- The skin should be soft and smooth to the touch, with enough natural oil in the tissues to keep it flexible.
- Some artificial creams and oils can block the pores and stop the skin from breathing properly.
- A yin face tends to be long and thin, coming to a point at the chin. A yang face tends to be round and the chin is square.
- A tall thin person is considered to have a yin build, while a smaller person of solid proportions is considered to have a yang build.

We inherit a lot of our characteristics from our parents, yet it is up to each of us to improve the quality of our health. Eating, drinking and breathing correctly can make an important difference to your life. You should try it, not because I say so, but simply because time and again it has been proven to work.

LFA T'ai Chi Sets

Over the next few pages I will introduce you to the following sets which we teach in all of our classes:

T'ai Chi Form
T'ai Chi Dance
T'ai Chi Stick
T'ai Chi Silk
T'ai Chi Sword
T'ai Chi Nunchaku
T'ai Chi Fan

Each part of the LFA Health Arts is designed to compliment the other, providing the mind, body and spirit with a complete strain free work out. When coupled with the Chang Ming diet the health improvements are multiplied many times.

We offer complete balance within our Arts
- The movements of our Form set are yin (close into the body), the breath we use is yang (using the whole of our lungs).
- Our Dance set uses yang movements (more flamboyant) and the breath we use is yin (using the upper part of our lungs).

T'ai Chi Long Life Diet

- Our K'ai Men and specialised breathing exercises were also developed thousands of years ago and are also taught as an important part of our arts.

In all LFA T'ai Chi classes, time is given to learning exactly where each movement starts and finishes. This is essential to the student's well being and ensuring that everyone who gives the time to learn, can gain the maximum benefit.

There is no time limit placed on learning any of our form sets, every person who comes into an LFA class is encouraged to progress at their own pace.

As with all the different sets in LFA T'ai Chi, the Stick and Silk are fun and a pleasure to learn. Initially everyone has their favourite set, I found the LFA T'ai Chi Sword the easiest set to learn. This fact made it my favourite in my early days of practising the Lee Family Arts. Now I can honestly say that I enjoy all aspects of the LFA Health Arts equally.

The longer I practise, the more I marvel about the connection between the different sets. The health

benefits never cease to amaze me.
It is the movements, the breathing and the Chang Ming diet which make the real difference. All we have to do is apply them, I know it is easy to say and far more difficult to put into practice. The benefits are there waiting for everyone who makes the effort.

It is always advisable to check that your instructor is a registered instructor with the LFA and not someone who has learnt their T'ai Chi without personal tuition from myself. The videos teach the first levels of T'ai Chi and are produced as a valuable teaching aid. For increased depth, you are most welcome to attend a LFA class, day course, Easter course, or summer course.

I often heard my late Master suggest to other people that they should try other styles and techniques for themselves - most of them came back to our Arts. Chee always told me that everything I needed could be found within the Lee Family Arts and I have always found this to be so. I have only ever studied one style and feel that with the best will in the world, if I had tried other styles, I would have brought some part of what I had learnt back with me.

I was asked by Chee to keep the essence of the Arts pure and I see that as being my vocation, along with helping other people. It is a role I feel very fortunate to have been requested to perform as I am able to work at something I love. The LFA association is growing and it will continue to grow, simply because the LFA Health Arts work.

An Instructor who teaches a class is there for the benefit of the students therefore instructors must ensure that they train daily (outside of their classes). I personally ensure that I train for a minimum period of two hours each day, usually between 5.00am and 7.00am I find this provides the foundation for the rest of my day.

LFA T'ai Chi Form

From your very first tentative movements of practising our T'ai Chi Form set, your mind, body and spirit will start to benefit. To the untrained eye, the movements appear soft, flowing and gentle, although there is far more involved than at first envisaged.

People have different conceptions about what T'ai chi really is. It was explained to me that the Lee Family Arts style of T'ai Chi has always been taught purely for health. If people wanted to train in a martial art they studied the Lee Family Art of Feng Shou (self defence).

There are many different styles of T'ai Chi to choose from, our style is based on Chinese medicine.
First we teach you the mechanics e.g. how to position your feet. This ensures correct weight distribution, good posture, and helps to ensure you are well rooted in order to gain the maximum benefit for your body. Of course, we are all different and the movements may be adapted if you have problems, say for example, with your knees or back.

Next we incorporate the arm movements - each movement is designed to harmonise with your feet movements.

When you feel truly comfortable with the hand and feet movements, try to harmonise your breathing. The type of breath we use in our Form set is a **yang breath**, which means we breathe deeply into the lower part of the lungs, thus cleansing them and removing the toxins which can sometimes accumulate through the normal western way of breathing.

Here are some of the dynamic effects which these deceptively simple actions of gentle movement and breathing can have on the whole of your system:

- Your blood will be encouraged to flow more freely around your body.
- Toxins will start to be expelled.
- Pressure will be taken off your vital organs.
- The mind will start to relax.

- all this from a few simple movements!

People often ask me what they can do for this ailment or that ailment. The simple answer is practise LFA T'ai Chi.

The LFA health arts are not a magic wand, however, the gentle movements set the wheels in motion for a healthier life style. We do not even need to understand how it works. How many of us know the full workings of a car? I don't, although I don't think twice about starting the engine and driving the car every day.

To the novice, I appreciate that it is difficult to understand how something, which appears to be nothing more than a sequence of soft flowing movements, can be responsible for some of the exceptional results which I have witnessed people experience through practising LFA T'ai Chi.

Although LFA T'ai Chi is easy on the body, it does in fact take patience whilst learning. It is different from most other types of exercise and the only way to learn it is by continuous repetition.

Often people who suffer from insomnia find they have the best nights sleep of the week after attending one of our many classes. Just think how much you could gain if you gave a little of your time each day to your training. The more time you are able to give to your training, the more you will gain.

The LFA Health Arts consists of more than our T'ai Chi Form set, although the Form provides the foundation for all of our other sets.

The Short Form consists of 50 movements which are fully explained on our T'ai Chi Form video.

The complete Form set consists of 140 movements, with each movement fully explained complete with photographs in our T'ai Chi Form book.

Both our books and videos are offered as optional teaching aids to help you revise and develop your training at your own pace.

T'ai Chi Dance

The LFA T'ai Chi Dance is designed to activate and stimulate the mind.

As previously mentioned, the movements of our T'ai Chi Dance are Yang. This means that they are more flamboyant when compared with those of the Form.

With the T'ai Chi Dance we first teach you the mechanics of how to move your feet, ensuring correct weight distribution. **Only when you have mastered the feet positions and have strong roots will you be able to gain from incorporating your arm movements.**

The third part of our learning process is to incorporate

the specialised breathing patterns which are an integral part of our Dance Set. To harness the special breathing techniques used in our Dance set, you should breathe in through the nose on the odd numbers and out through the mouth on the even numbers. However, unlike the other T'ai Chi sets, the breath does not sink to the lower part of the lungs.

Our T'ai Chi Dance is not a dance that is usually practised to music, although, it can be. Its roots are based in the five elements including their respective colours, and Li energy. It is made up of a sequence of soft flowing movements which move at a much faster pace than our Form set.

The yin breath associated with our Dance set activates and stimulates the mind, therefore it is ideal to practise when your get up and go has got up and gone. It is important not to practise our Dance set before going to bed, otherwise you will have a sleepless night.

Whereas our T'ai Chi Form works on mainly developing your internal energy (Chi), the Dance works on harnessing the external energy called Li energy. The Dance can at first appear to be a little more demanding than our Form set and this is why all beginners start by learning the T'ai Chi Form. The Dance is added as you reach the next stage whereby you are able to benefit from harmonising the Li energy with your own developing Chi energy.

There are 184 movements in our T'ai Chi Dance set, each movement is fully explained complete with photographs in the LFA T'ai Chi Dance Book. Our Dance video teaches you the first fifty movements in an easy to follow format.

I practise the Dance first thing every morning, and find it is an excellent tonic to set myself up for the rest of the day.

T'ai Chi Stick

The LFA T'ai Chi Stick set is a sequence of beautiful flowing movements designed to improve your health, balance, co-ordination and reflexes.

It is important to progress slowly at your own pace. We should always remember that true progress relates to the quality of the movements which you practise and not to the quantity that you know. It tends to be a Western concept to judge our proficiency, by the amount we know. The LFA Health Arts are an eastern art and a different approach is applied. It is not what the person next to you is doing that counts; it is what is going on inside your own body.

Our Stick Set is not competitive in nature, nor is it aggressive, its movements are used to improve the quality of your life.

It is important to learn your stances first, applying the principles of the Taoist Walk, only when your stances are fully grounded should you bring your stick into play.

It is best if you have your own stick (we normally practise using a broom handle), because in our health arts we work with the body's natural energy. Your own energy will pass into the wood and you will gain more from the Stick set by using a wooden broom handle (not a plastic one).

Hold your stick lightly, allowing it to move freely between your hands. If you hold on to your stick too tightly you will restrict the flow of your natural energy.

If you have difficulty with your balance, then the movements which require you to stand on one leg may be practised in Cat stance (your heel is raised with the ball of your foot resting lightly on the floor). A fully qualified LFA instructor will be able to help you adapt movements, ensuring that you receive the maximum health benefits.

Physiotherapists have recommended the LFA Stick set. A few years ago a retired gentleman came into one of my classes unable to fasten or unfasten the top button of his shirt. After practising the LFA T'ai Chi Stick for approximately four weeks, he found his top button no longer presented a problem.

There are 270 movements in our Stick set, the first one hundred and fifty are fully explained and photographed in volume one of our T'ai Chi Stick book. The first fifty movements are explained in an easy to follow format on our T'ai Chi Stick video. Within the LFA we aim to provide a full professional service to everyone, who wishes to benefit from our Arts

T'ai Chi Silk

Our T'ai Chi Silk set offers a complete series of soft flowing movements which are designed to help you find the softness and the circles in the movements. People interested in losing weight should practise our T'ai Chi Silk set continually for twenty minutes three times per week. Like the T'ai Chi Stick, it also helps to improve your balance and co-ordination, which in turn improves the quality of your health.

Quite often, it is the men who enjoy the Silk most, yet when they are asked to bring a silk to the class their facial expressions are often priceless!
A student once commented "Who needs aerobics, when we have the Silk".
The movements are learnt slowly, first learning the stances and incorporating the Taoist Walk. Next, we add the flowing movements of the Silk, subtly working the upper body, neck, shoulders, arms, wrists and fingers.

Once the movements have been learnt and the correct breathing patterns adopted the Silk is practised a little faster. However, this stage does not happen until the student is able to cope with it.

There are 156 movements in our T'ai Chi Silk set, each one is fully explained and photographed in our T'ai Chi Silk book. The first 50 movements are explained in an easy to follow format on our T'ai Chi Silk video.

I hope you too will find the pleasure which I experience when practising the LFA Silk set. It is something special and is to be cherished.

You will find that the LFA Silk Set is taught in all official LFA classes,

T'ai Chi Sword

The LFA T'ai Chi Sword improves your health, balance, co-ordination and concentration.

When I first started to learn T'ai Chi, I found that of all the different sets, the movements of the Sword set were the easiest to learn - that is until I found the concentration and control over the mind and the body required to practise the first half of the Sword set correctly.

The first 108 movements of the LFA T'ai Chi Sword

set are practised at the same speed as the LFA T'ai Chi Form. An experienced students should be able to practise our Sword set along side someone who is practising the LFA T'ai Chi Form and both should move together as one breath. This can take many hours of pleasant, dedicated practise.

I mentioned above that the concentration and control was only applied to the first half of the Sword set, in the second part you move like the wind.

The whole set alternates between Yin and Yang and the second part requires a different type of training.

This is what makes the LFA Health Arts so special. It works on every part of the mind, body and spirit.

There are 216 movements in our T'ai Chi Sword set, the first 108 movements are fully explained and photographed in the LFA T'ai Chi Sword book. The first 50 movements are fully explained in an easy to follow format in our T'ai Chi Sword video. Over the years we have had many letters from all over the country thanking us for producing our series of videos. They are a valuable teaching aid to people who are unable to attend regular classes.

T'ai Chi Nunchaku

The Nunchaku, (which are two short sticks joined by cord or chain), are usually thought of as a deadly weapon. I hasten to add that we allow only the foam, safety cord ones to be used in our classes, and they are not used as a weapon.

This is one set whose **foundations** have been taken from the martial art side of our Arts. The movements are soft and flowing, they improve your health, balance, co-ordination and are excellent for improving the reflexes. This is due to the variety of stances used, and the continuous throwing and catching of the nunchaku.

More than any of our other sets, the Nunchaku brings a smile to every practitioners face. Whether they secretly think of themselves as Bruce Lee or not, I don't know, although I do know that a lot of dedication goes into mastering this set.

We have people over 80 years of age practising the LFA Nunchaku set, alongside students in their teens. The opening and closing of the fingers as the

Nunchaku are caught and released, and exercises the whole of the hands. Benefit is also felt in the upper body, and the legs as you move through the combination of required stances.

As with all of our Sets, no strain is placed on the body and the movements can be adapted for you (if so required), by an experienced LFA instructor, to suit your personal needs.

Students are only taught the Nunchaku once they have learnt 50 movements in all of the other disciplines.

People who attend mixed ability classes eagerly await the time when they too may start to learn this impressive looking set.

The movements flow at an average speed, although it is easy for a group of students to get carried away, when left to practise on their own. The effect is similar to that of a runaway train. It is then important to slow the movements down a little so that the true benefits can be felt.

We have not produced a video on the LFA Nunchaku set as yet, this is a project for a later date. However, we have produced a book which covers the first 150 movements in full detail. Each position is photographed making it easy for you to follow.

Your greatest knowledge of our Nunchaku set will be

gained from learning from a qualified LFA instructor, or with myself at one of the many day courses or workshops which I hold throughout the year. If, because of your circumstances, you are unable to attend a class or day course, I suggest you start slowly and give yourself plenty of time to understand the subtleties of our Nunchaku Set.

LFA T'ai Chi Fan

Most ladies appear to particularly like the sound of the LFA T'ai Chi Fan set. In reality it is the most difficult and most demanding of all of our sets.

The T'ai Chi Fan set requires stamina and the ability to be able to get up and down off the floor gracefully (while opening and closing your Fan). Our Fan set incorporates the stances from the T'ai Chi, K'ai Men, Feng Shou and Chi Shu. It incorporates kicks, rolls and specialised breathing techniques.

Because of the techniques required to master our Fan Set, it is only taught to very advanced students. Although, as with all of our sets, we recommend that if you cannot physically practise the movements, you can mentally practise them and incorporate the breathing techniques.

The Fans which we use in our classes are made of bamboo and silk, my own personal Fan is made of Chinese steel and silk.

When practising the Fan we adopt the same teaching methods which are taught with all of our sets. First learn the stances, (it is a good idea to work in blocks of ten movements). Next, it is important to master the hand movements of the Fan.

It is not until you have mastered the first 20 movements, that the Fan becomes more demanding. The use of stances such as chicken, drunkard, fish, turtle, and praying mantis all come into play.

When you feel comfortable with the hands and feet movements of the fan set, we add in the breathing. Throughout all of our form sets, we breathe in through the nose on the odd numbers and out through the mouth on the even numbers.

I cannot emphasise enough, the importance of knowing where each movement starts and finishes. This applies to all the different sets which we teach. If you cut a movement short, you will not achieve the health benefits which are associated with that particular part.

The LFA Fan set certainly gives the body a complete physical and mental work out. Because of the stamina required, our Fan set, it is not taught in our classes. The Fan Set is taught under my personal supervision, to ensure that the students are able to cope with this slightly more demanding set.

There are 300 movements in the whole of the Fan Set and it is the longest set in the LFA Health Arts.

There is not a video for the Fan set, nor will there be. This is because the Fan is not recommended for beginners. However, we have produced a book to help students who wish to use it as a learning aid. The book contains the first 150 movements and each position is carefully explained and photographed, making it easy to follow. **As with all of our sets please consult your doctor before taking part in our exercise programmes.**

K'ai Men Exercises

K'ai Men (which means open door) is an art within itself and is taught within all of our classes. The art of K'ai Men was first introduced into China by the Sons of Reflected Light and we have them to thank for the wonderful benefits of this branch of our arts.

The healing aspects of K'ai Men are found in meridian healing, vibration, pulsation, sound and meditation. Great importance is placed on using the correct breathing techniques in all of our K'ai Men exercises.

Our lives begin and end with deep breathing. Deep breathing involves bringing harmony between Yin and Yang and it also includes vibration. We place great importance on the how to learn to breathe deeply at all times, as this will ensure good health by fully oxygenating the blood, so that the heart is not overworked.

Regulating your breathing under controlled conditions will help you to sink your breath lower, helping to ignite your Chi energy which is stored in the Tan Tien (an area just below your navel).

In the physical part of our K'ai Men exercises, emphasis is placed on complete mind control of the movement. This part of the exercise is called the extension.

Tao Yin breathing principles are based on Yin and Yang and abide by the rules of the five elements. All of this gives the practitioner tremendous ability to create harmony between the organs in the body. Tao Yin means 'Secret Island', which basically explains the dynamic effect this type of breathing can have on the health of your body, mind and spirit. People who worry about memory loss should regularly practise K'ai Men exercises as the process increases the mental capacity of the brain and allows greater mind control.

I often hear people say that they do not have enough time to train or they feel they are running around like headless chickens trying to fit a little more into their day. Our exercises help to calm the mind and put the pressures of life in a more orderly context, it makes sense to practise them.

People in the Western world tend to use only shallow breathing, and therefore they are robbing themselves of the beauty that a world of good health truly has to offer.

The exercises in the LFA K'ai Men exercise books can make a difference if you give them a chance.

Breathing Exercises

The LFA teach specialised breathing exercises which are very gentle and use flowing movements.

With these exercises, it is important to practise them very slowly, harmonising the movements with your breathing.

In our classes we also teach students about the connection points between the body's energy centres and the exercise we are practising.

The LFA are able to offer exercises for the relief of various ailments and our book on breathing exercises is also available so that everyone may practise them in the comfort of their own home.

Living the Taoist Way

There are many theories on Taoism. People have spent much time and effort trying to translate historical Chinese documents. We may find this information helpful although the only way in which it is possible to fully understand the way of the Tao, is to live it. This involves living as close as possible to a natural way of life.

If we are preoccupied with the accumulation of possessions and can think no further than the material side of life, we cannot claim to be living in accordance with the will of the Tao.
If you find yourself in a privileged position, enjoy it and help others who are less fortunate than yourself.

Taoism is about the natural way of things and incorporates the balance of Yin and Yang plus the five elements. The ancient Taoists learnt that where there is a beginning, there would also be an ending. Where there is an ending, there is also the beginning of something new. From a maximum level, there must be a decline to a minimum level and of course the opposite also applies. This continuous change is the natural order of things according to the laws of the Tao.

It is important not to waste our time here on earth, therefore it is not by chance that you have found the LFA Health Arts. Once you have started to develop along the right lines, you will find you are laying the foundations for the future. If you live closer to the balance within nature it will lead you to the laws of the universe. As you evolve it may appear that your world has completely changed, in reality it is you that has changed. You will be able to see the good in the world and not the negativity that tends to plague people in these modern day times.

For people who follow a Taoist way of life, the very beginning of age relevance begins at 70, promising a time of joy and freedom. It's a time to reap the rewards of your efforts, your wisdom and experience and this should prove invaluable to you and your family.

If you have adhered to eating the Chang Ming way, you should experience very few health problems. This is because you have laid careful foundations for your old age. You will glow with vitality and the healthy looks of your mature years. People who are already 50 or 60 years of age, can still attain good health and no one should consider themselves too old to change their eating habits. At the end of the day, everyone has choices, if you decide that you do not wish to alter your eating habits and that you would rather continue with the modern day pre-packaged food, both the LFA and myself respect your decision. We are always here to help you whenever you choose to contact us.

The Tao

My late Master used to say "Sit back and watch the Tao at work". This is easier said than done.

We all want everything, when we want it, yet our pre-set ideas often cause us stress. If it is meant for us, it will happen, for those of us who follow the Tao know that everything will be provided. That does not mean you sit back and do nothing, on the contrary, we must take part in life.

The previous statement is not a contradiction in terms. The Tao just is.

The Tao is the way of all things - the day which follows night, the summer which follows winter. We take for granted all of these things, yet in accepting these facts we accept the way of the Tao because the Tao is everything and the Tao is nothing.

People debate Taoism, trying hard to understand its principles. I was taught that in doing this, one takes himself or herself out of the flow of the Tao. During my own personal training I eventually learnt not to question everything. Although I must admit, I did not find this an easy lesson to learn. In fact, most of the lessons I have learnt were not the ones I thought I was going to learn.

T'ai Chi Long Life Diet

The Tao is the strength and weakness of all situations. It is the good and bad. Yet everyone who truly understand the way of the Tao realise that neither good nor bad really exists.

We all walk a path for which there is no map, at least not in the normal sense of the word. Everyone can find the Tao within themselves. It requires an open mind and one that does not allow analysis to invade the brain.

It will make little difference to the Tao whether we believe in the Tao or not, the only difference it makes is to ourselves. For in dismissing the Tao, we automatically reject the natural order of the universe. Can you honestly say that day does not follow night, season does not follow season. Man often thinks he can improve on the work of the Tao creating what is called improvements, yet for every improvement which is created, a defect is automatically created. We only have to look to the news to see reports of the leap forwards in modern day medicine. The same news often reports on the side effects of such improvements.

Chee Soo explained in his book 'The Taoist Ways Of Healing' - that the Taoists of China knew that in their infinite wisdom, they could not give a different individualistic description to everything that existed. To cover the enormity of the task, and to describe the Will of the Supreme Spirit, they gave it the simplest of names – the Tao, which explains everything and yet, in its own typical Chinese way, describes nothing.

Yin and Yang

Yin signifies all things that are negative. Watch the news today and see how much negativity they can report in one programme. How many times is good news reported?

It has been said that over 75 % of the world's population lean towards the yin side of life. This suggests that over 75% of the world's population is out of balance with Yin and Yang, therefore out of flow with the Tao.

Yin also represents female and Yang represents male, like the two sides of a coin. Yin and Yang represent opposite sides, although you will always find an element of Yin within Yang, and visa versa. An example of Yin and Yang can be found if we look at the seasons, summer represents Yang, yet it is possible for rain to fall within summer representing Yin.

Traditionally Yin represents femininity, body, soul, earth, moon, night, water, dark, cold, contraction, and centripetal motion. Yang represents masculinity, mind, spirit, heaven, sun, day, fire, heat, daylight, expansion and centrifugal motion.

Duality applies to everything within the universe, it is important to remember that, every half has a bottom and a top, also a back and a front and so it goes on. Everything is one within itself, while at the same time everything contains both Yin and Yang elements.

I cannot state strongly enough that Taoism is not some mystical religion, come to that, it is not a religion at all. It is an understanding of nature. 'It simply is.'

To attain good health it is up to each of us to ensure that our body is in harmony, a correct balance of Yin and Yang. We cannot be blamed for the deterioration of our health if we do not understand the natural way, it is up to each of us to make a start and seek this 'way' rather than put things off until tomorrow.

The accuracy of the observations made by the Ancient Taoists can be seen in the yearly calendar which they devised. It was so accurate that it only had to be adjusted every sixty years, instead of every four years like our western calendar. If modern day man paused in his constant desire to attain knowledge, he would understand that the answers were discovered long ago by the Ancient Taoists. They are readily available to us if we choose to take the same path.

The Taoists learned to live with nature every single day of their lives.

The Five Elements

The Chinese learnt long ago the importance of the five elements and the relationship it has to our health and the way we live today. It does not matter if we understand the five elements. If we are experiencing difficulties in our lives then we are out of balance with the five elements, which also means we are out of balance with Yin and Yang. Because one is linked to the other and this in turn is related to the Tao, it is understandable that the five elements are used in treating illness.

The five elements were explained by my late Master, Chee Soo, as follows:-
Fire
Wood
Earth
Metal
Water
The corresponding cures are listed below: -
Fire   Spiritual Cure
Wood   Chang Ming
Earth   Herbal Therapy
Metal   Acupuncture
Water   Thermogenesis

Each element gives way to the next, for example wood is food for the fire, when it becomes ash it is food for the earth. From the earth comes metal, now metal in its molten liquid form is like water, which is nourishment for the trees, which gives us wood, which feeds the fire.

Although it can be explained that each element gives way to the other, each element can also destroy the other. For example metal can cut down wood, wood can take nourishment from the earth, earth can absorb or damn water, fire turns water to vapour.

SPIRITUAL CURE (fire)
This is achieved by correct eating and drinking, living closer to nature and following the unwritten laws of the universe. It means trying to help others along the pathway. It means saying your prayers regularly to say thank you.

CHANG MING (wood)
This is the Taoist way of eating naturally and drinking correctly, it will cure the majority of illness (provided they are caught in time). If you are not on the Chang Ming diet and catch even one cold a year, you can avoid further ailments by adopting this diet.

HERBAL THERAPY (earth)
Herbs have long played a part in Chinese Medicine and they are still as important today. The Chinese have far greater knowledge in this field than most other countries.

ACUPUNCTURE (metal)
Acupuncture has become more recognised in the West over recent years, although this ancient craft has been used in China for many years. It involves inserting needles at specific energy points or meridians in the body.

THERMOGENESIS (water)
This involves the use of heat and can take many formats, for example the ginger compress, or the ancient art of cupping.

It is very important to be able to cure, it is even more important to understand the cause. This is the thinking behind the LFA Health Arts, we do not want to cover a problem with a plaster, we wish to eliminate the cause of the problem.

Chang Ming (health diet)

If you are truly interested in good health and evolving as a person to a deeper level of understanding, then you need to adopt the Chang Ming diet. We should all take the responsibility for our own health.

I have witnessed people approach my late Master, Chee Soo, with various health problems and his first question was always "are you on the diet?" if they hadn't heard of the diet he would explain the importance of it.

I am not however saying you cannot benefit from practising the LFA Health Arts if you are not on the diet, I am merely explaining that if you wish to take them to a far deeper level there is no short cut and the Chang Ming diet is an important part of your evolution. We as individuals have to be prepared to help ourselves. No one can do it for us.

As mentioned before, at first sight the Chang Ming diet does not appear to be an easy diet to follow, but with time and this recipe book, it becomes easier.

Basically, there are two lists of food, one showing foods which can be eaten and another showing foods which should not be eaten. However, there are always exceptions, for example a colleague of mine found that she was allergic to wheat. This means that she has had to experiment with different types of flour to make pastry and bread. Another person may be allergic to any type of dairy produce or, if a person is temporally suffering from a Yang complaint, it may need to be treated by adding a Yin food to their diet, on a temporary basis. However, this cure for a Yang ailment may not be affective if they are eating a normal western diet.

My husband and myself have followed the Chang Ming diet for many years. Neither of us broke it for over eight years and when did break it, it was inadvertantly. Now, I have to admit, that occasionally if I eat out, I cannot guarantee that the food is Chang Ming no matter how hard I try. However, we always eat strictly Chang Ming at home.

A person who follows the Chang Ming diet will find that they have more energy and find they only need between five and six hours sleep each night.

It is important that you never eat too much and should never leave the table feeling bloated. Another important factor is to chew your food really well; each mouthful should be chewed until it is like water, if possible.

If you are eating food without additives and preservatives then the body does not require a huge amount of fluid to flush the kidneys out. The Chinese taught that too much fluid puts a strain on your kidneys. If you are concerned about your kidneys then you should drink parsley tea.

Chee Soo stated "if you are ill then you need to change your diet", it is as simple as that, or are you happy being ill?

When following the Chang Ming diet it only takes about 10 days for you to first start noticing a difference in your health. However, there are some points to note, for example if you are used to drinking a large amount of fluid you may experience some constipation. Although you are eating well you may lose weight, this is nothing to worry about. Your body will settle down to its natural weight for you. My husband lost one and a half stone during his first month of eating the Chang Ming way. If you experience any aches and pains, make a note of them, this is the body ridding itself of toxins. You may also experience slight mood swings or headaches, again this is the body cleansing itself of the toxins. Like any diet you need to eat the correct balance of vitamins, proteins and minerals. It also helps to include correct breathing patterns and practise your LFA T'ai Chi training.

If you cut your meals down to hardly any food this

will not help you to lose weight in the long run. It is important, to eat sensibly at least twice a day and you should not eat between meals.

This diet is not some latest fad; it has been around for thousands of years. It is a way of life, and once you incorporate it into yours, you will find a new world within the one you already live in.

Chee Soo stated that even the most serious complaint could be beaten so that the person may be brought back to good health. That is, of course, providing that the body has not been allowed to deteriorate to such a low level that it can no longer be helped. It is important to remember that there is always hope.

Two of the worst ways to make your body useless is the intake of drugs and unnecessary operations.

- Eat only when hungry and not just out of habit
- Eat more grains and vegetables
- Chew your food really well
- Do not over eat at any time
- Reduce your liquid intake

Remember it takes three years of strictly eating the Chang Ming way, before your body can be considered to be healthy, the bones and teeth are a different matter and this could take at least ten years of eating the Chang Ming way.

Some people start eating the Chang Ming way then wander by the wayside, if you go astray simply start again. You will receive more benefit than not eating Chang Ming at all.

IT IS ACCEPTABLE TO WEAN YOURSELF ONTO THE DIET STARTING WITH TWO OR MORE DAYS EACH WEEK.

In the pages which follow, I have offered some easy to follow recipes. If you know how to cook please bear with me, for I have written this book with a special friend of mine in mind, who claims to have no idea about cooking!

Food Types Which May Be Eaten

1. Anything made from natural, whole grains which has not been refined e.g.
Brown rice, buckwheat, wheat, barley, millet, rye, maize and includes bread, cakes, puddings, biscuits, breakfast foods etc.
2. All organically grown vegetables that are in season, especially root vegetables (<u>EXCLUDING</u> THOSE ON THE LIST OF FOODS WHICH MAY NOT BE EATEN).
3. Sprouted beans (mung, soya, alfalfa etc.).
4. Seaweed.
5. Locally grown fruits and berries.
6. Nuts, preferably roasted (not salted).
7. Low fat natural yoghurt.
8. Honey.
9. Cottage Cheese or Vegetarian cheese.
10. Herb teas and China teas.
11. Vegetable margarine and oils e.g. sunflower, sesame, safflower.
12. Eggs, scrambled or in omelettes (cakes etc.).
13. Natural sea salt, sesame seed salt, soya sauce.
14. All dried fruit- raisins, currents, apricots etc.
15. All grain milks, soya milk and coconut milk.

16. Herbs.
17. Drinks extracted from freshly grown vegetables (ideally make your own).
18. Soya products.
    Utilise The Following If Necessary
19. Non fat fish (EXCLUDING THOSE ON THE LIST OF FOODS WHICH MAY NOT BE EATEN).
20. Seafood, shrimps, prawns etc. (Be wary of crabmeat).
21. Wild birds, pigeons, pheasants etc.
22. Wild or free range chicken, turkey etc.
23. Skimmed milk or powdered skimmed milk.

Food Types Which Are Not To Be Eaten

1. Refined and processed foods, if artificial colourings, preservatives, flavourings are added, avoid them.
2. Any grain foods which have been processed, especially white bread and anything made from white flour.
3. All deep fried foods.
4. Coffee, alcohol, tobacco, chocolate and other sweets
5. Spices, rock salt, mustard, pepper, vinegar, pickles, curry.

6. Meat such as pork, beef, mutton and lamb.
7. Salmon, mackerel, shark, swordfish, tuna and whale.
8. Sugar.
9. Ice-cream.
10. Potatoes, tomatoes, aubergines, rhubarb, spinach. (THE FIRST THREE ARE MEMBERS OF THE DEADLY NIGHTSHADE FAMILY and contain poisons called glyco alkaloids. Some people can neutralise these toxins as they pass through the body, others may use up a lot of their life force trying to rid themselves of such sub stances. When your life force is depleted, that is when major ailments appear and the body's immune system breaks down through being overloaded).
11. Concentrated meat extracts.
12. Milk, cheese, butter, dairy yoghurt, boiled or fried eggs.
13. Lard or dripping which comes from animal fats.
14. Any bird or fish which has a lot of fat tissue.
15. Tropical fruit (these are very yin and contain a lot of acid) bananas are an exception because they do not contain juice but should be eaten in moderation.

CHANG MING

The Three Thousand Year Old Health Diet for the Beginner

This section is for everyone who says 'I can't cook'. To that statement I say "have confidence in yourself". Cooking is like everything else, it takes practise, the more you practise, the easier it becomes.

So lets start at the very beginning and learn together. The only difference between you and I is that I've been doing it longer. If I can cook, anyone can!

First we need a shopping list. This can be split into two parts

> List 1. Food for the cupboard
> List 2. Food with a limited life span

To some people, quantities may be a problem. That is easily taken care of - if we assume you are cooking for one; for two persons simply double the quantities.

Because the ingredients in list 1. are not classed as perishable, you can build your stocks gradually. Here are some examples of foods in list 1.

List 1
Dried beans (kidney, black-eyed, broad, chickpeas etc.).

Tinned beans can make life easier (although rinse them thoroughly before using).

- Lentils (all types i.e. red, yellow, brown) Note: red lentils are particularly tasty.
- Dried Fruits (all types).
- Grains, brown rice, millet, bulgur wheat, couscous.
- Unsalted nuts.
- Seeds, sunflower, pumpkin etc.
- Flours, wholemeal, maize, barley, rye, buckwheat, soya etc. (Self raising wholemeal flour makes life easier for cakes).
- Cereal - muesli (check ingredients on packet or mix your own), shredded wheat, porridge.
- Wholemeal noodles (instant ones may be purchased in some supermarkets).
- Honey.
- Dried skimmed milk, or soya (check life span on carton).
- Dried herbs (keep out of sunlight).
- Herb teas.
- Carob powder (substitute for chocolate).
- Cooking oil sunflower, sesame (unrefined is best).
- Soy sauce.
- Tahini (made from ground sesame seeds - can be made from toasted or untoasted seeds).

- Whole fruit, sugarless jam (available from health stores and some supermarkets)
- Yeast extract, malt extract
- Dried seaweed
- Dried bean curd

List 2

Now we come to list 2 i.e. foods with a limited life span, these include some of the following:

- Vegetables (organic are best)
- Locally grown fruit (products of this country)
- Fresh herbs
- Bean sprouts
- Vegetarian cheese or cottage cheese
- Sunflower margarine
- Wholemeal bread
- Bean curd (tofu)
- Free range eggs
- Poultry (low fat white meat)
- White fish

To produce the recipes in this book you will also need the following items: -

rolling pin,   mixing bowl,
baking tray,   oven proof casserole dishes,

wok or deep frying pan,	saucepans,
garlic press,	scales,
air tight containers,	sandwich cake tins,
vegetable knife,	vegetable brush (for scrubbing),
pastry brush,	hot food flask (if you intend to eat out midday),
grater,	blender (optional)
8" cake tin	

Centuries ago, it was found that by following this diet you only needed to eat twice a day, this allows the correct amount of time for the body to digest food and rest before the next meal. For people who prefer to eat three times a day, I have allowed for this in my sample menus.

Grains

Grains play a very important role in our daily diet. With this in mind, I have included my recipe for multi grain cookies. These can be made once a week and stored in an airtight container. They are simple to make and with practice they take five minutes to prepare, and 10 to 15 minutes to bake in the oven.

Multi Grain Cookies- - pre heat oven 400f/200c, gas mark 6

Ingredients
4oz 120g sunflower margarine
4oz 120g honey
2oz 60g oatmeal flakes
4oz 120g mixed flours (maize, rye, buckwheat, soya, wholemeal, barley, brown rice flour)

1. Place the margarine and honey into a mixing bowl, cream (stir) together
2. Add the oats and stir together
3. Add the mixed flours, stir well
4. Kneed together to form a ball, add a little more flour if the mixture is too sticky
5. Lightly sprinkle flour onto a work surface, roll out the mixture until it is approximately 3/16 an inch thick (4mm), cut to shape with pastry cutter
6. Grease a baking tray, place the cookies on the tray and bake them in a pre-heated oven, cook for approx 10-15 minutes, or until golden. (The cookies will be soft when they come out of the oven, allow them to set before removing them from the baking tray)

You can vary the flavours by adding 1oz of sunflower and pumpkin seeds, or dried fruit (add these ingredients when you add the flour: see 3).

Basic Sponge - pre heat oven 300fh/180c, Gas Mark 4

This recipe includes soya flour which is an excellent form of protein however this can be substituted with wholemeal flour.

3oz 90g wholemeal, self-raising flour
1oz 30g soya flour
2 free range eggs (beaten)
3oz 90g honey
4oz 120g margarine

1. Place the honey and margarine into a mixing bowl and cream together.
2. Add the eggs and flour, mix well
3. Add a little cold water if the mixture is too stiff
4. Place the mixture in a sandwich cake tin
5. Bake in the oven for approx 15-20 minutes. (To check if the sponge is cooked properly, lightly touch the top of the sponge with your finger, the

sponge is cooked when the surface springs back
to its original position).

SHORT CUT
Double the quantities, divide mixture into two halves,
add mixed fruit to one half and 1oz 30g of carob
powder (to give a chocolate flavour) to the other half.
Store the sponges in an airtight container or
alternatively, divide them into individual portions
and freeze.

Sample Menus for Everyday of the Week with Step-by-Step Instructions

Seaweed should be eaten everyday as part of your Chang Ming diet as it is rich in minerals. I personally use wakama sushi nori which is available from health food shops. It comes in sheets and I toast one sheet, crumble it then divide it between my husband and myself with our main meal of the day.

Day One

Breakfast - Shredded wheat, soya or skimmed milk, wholemeal toast, honey or sugar free jam, herb tea.

Lunch - Easy vegetable soup, wholemeal bread bap, multi grain cookies, herb tea.

Evening Meal -Onion crumble, stir-fried vegetables, roast parsnips, carob pudding with maize custard, (slimmers should substitute a baked apple for their dessert), herb tea.

Breakfast is the easiest meal of the day to take care of - everything can be bought pre packaged. The more adventurous people can make their own bread.

Lunch - preparation of easy vegetable soup takes only a few minutes; again, it becomes easier through practise. My ingredients are approximate and may be adapted to suit your individual tastes and needs.

Easy Vegetable Soup

1 carrot washed scrubbed and chopped
1 onion peeled and chopped
2 sticks of celery scrubbed and chopped
2 radishes scrubbed and sliced
1/2 pt boiling water
1/2 teaspoon of yeast extract or a vegetable stock cube
Small pinch of parsley
Small pinch of sage

1. Place all the ingredients in a pan and bring to the boil. Turn the heat down and simmer for fifteen minutes. Blend if you prefer a smooth, thicker soup

SHORTCUT

You can now buy some whole food soups which conform to the Chang Ming diet, although you must check the ingredients on the labels.

Evening Meal

Onion Crumble - pre heat oven 375f/190c gas mark 5

8oz 240g onions peeled and chopped
1 clove garlic, crushed
Water to cover the onions
1 tablespoon tahini
1 pinch sage
Soy sauce to taste
Crumble
1 oz 30g oats
2 oz 60g mixed flours
1-2 tablespoons of sunflower oil

1. Place the onions in a pan; use just enough water to cover them. Cook gently for approx 6 minutes
2. Stir in the tahini, garlic and sage

3. Season with soy sauce.

Crumble
4. Mix the dry ingredients together, then add the oil
5. Grease an oven proof dish
6. Transfer the onion mixture to the dish
7. Sprinkle the crumble mixture on top of the onions
8. Bake for 20-30 minutes

Roast Parsnips

2 medium sized parsnips scrubbed or peeled (cut both ends off)

1. Cut the parsnips into roast potato size chunks
2. Place them on a greased baking tray
3. Roast them in the oven until tender and golden
SHORT CUT. PRE-BOIL THE PARSNIPS UNTIL TENDER, THEN ROAST IN THE OVEN UNTIL GOLDEN

Stir Fried Mixed Vegetables
(DOUBLE THE INGREDIENTS TO MAKE ENOUGH FOR TOMORROW'S VEGETABLE PIE FILLING)
2 medium mushrooms washed, scrubbed and chopped

1 small onion peeled and chopped
1 courgette washed and chopped
1 small carrot washed, scrubbed and chopped
Soy sauce to taste

Note: Why not make up your own combination?

1. Heat 1-2 tablespoons of sunflower oil in a wok or deep frying pan. **(If slimming, omit the oil, use a non stick wok, increase the quantity of mushrooms which will increase the quantity of liquid in the pan / wok).**

2. Add the vegetables (stirring them a few times). Turn down the heat to 200F/400°C Gas mark 6 and cook for 5-10 minutes for crunchy vegetables, or longer if preferred. Lightly cooked vegetables retain more of their vitamins and minerals. When cold, store the surplus stir fried vegetables in a sealed container in a refridgerator, so that they can be used for Day Two's Vegetable Pie.

If slimming, substitute a baked apple instead of maize custard and carob pudding.

Baked Apple

1. Core an apple and place it in an oven proof dish.
2. Fill half of centre with raisins
3. Add a teaspoon of honey on top of raisins
4. Fill rest of centre with raisins
5. Bake in the oven until it is soft,
   (approx.10 minutes) **(375f/190c gas mark 5)**

Maize Custard

1/4 pint milk, soya or skimmed
2 tablespoons maize flour

Honey to taste

1. Mix the maize flour to a paste with a little of the cold milk
2. Bring the rest of the milk to the boil in a sauce pan
3. Stir the maize paste into the sauce pan
4. Continue stirring until the custard thickens (if the custard does not thicken, remove the pan from the heat, mix some more maize flour with cold milk, add it to the pan and return the pan to heat, continue stirring until the custard thickens)
5. Add honey to taste

Carob Pudding - simply use a piece of the carob cake (made previously) from the basic sponge recipe see page 83 and 84.
Then cover with maize custard.

Day Two

Breakfast - Porridge, wholemeal toast, herbal or green tea (available from Chinese supermarkets and some Healthfood shops).

Lunch - Wholemeal sandwiches, fruit cake, herbal tea.

Evening Meal - Vegetable and Soya mince pie (chicken or turkey mince may be used), salad, multi grain cookies, herbal tea.

Breakfast - This is easily taken care of, - follow the instructions on the packet for porridge - add honey to taste.

Lunch

Wholemeal Sandwich

2 slices of wholemeal bread
Sunflower margarine - optional
Filling suggestions - Tahini and cucumber, cottage cheese and cress, cold sliced vegetarian sausage, chicken, turkey, and mushroom pate. Why not make up your own combination?

Slimmers should only have two slices of bread, try and cut out the margarine and add plenty of salad. Look for low fat dressings; add an apple to your lunch if you still feel hungry. Finish with a small piece of fruit cake, if you are still hungry eat a banana or low fat yoghurt.

Fruit Cake - See basic sponge recipe on page 83

Evening Meal

SHORT CUT
Make enough pastry to make a vegetable and mince pie, plus a cheese and onion pie and an apple pie for tomorrow's lunch.

Wholemeal Pastry - Pre heat oven 400f/200c, gas mark 6
8oz 240g wholemeal self raising flour
4oz 120g sunflower margarine
cold water to mix

1. Place the flour and margarine into a mixing bowl
2. Rub the margarine into the flour with fingers (until it resembles a bread crumb texture)
3. Add water (a little at a time) mixing well with a knife
4. Divide pastry into three equal parts

The following pies will bake together, bake until golden:

Vegetable and Mince Pie

- If using soya mince, use 2oz 60g (see packet for instructions), if using poultry, lightly cook in 1 tablespoon of sunflower oil.
- Use ready cooked stir fried vegetables from the previous evenings' meal (mix with the mince).
- Grease a small plate.
- Sub-divide (one of the sections of pastry in two parts, one piece slightly larger than the other). Roll out the largest piece on floured surface.
- Line a greased plate with the pastry (Note: to transfer the pastry to the plate, wrap the pastry around the rolling pin and then unroll the pastry over the plate, trim off the surplus).

- Place the vegetable and mince mix on top of the pastry lined plate.
- Roll out the remainder of the pastry, cover the filling with the pastry lid.
- Brush the top of the pie with a little milk to glaze. Cook until golden brown (about 15 to 20 minutes).

Vegetable Pie - As above, only omit the mince.

Cheese and Onion Pie

4oz 120g grated vegetarian cheese (slimmers use low fat cheese)
1 small onion peeled and chopped
2oz 60g cooked brown rice or cooked turnip
small pinch of sage
soy sauce to taste

1. Mix all the ingredients together then follow the method for the Vegetable and Mince Pie

Apple Pie

1 large bramley apple (you can use desert apples and leave the skins on, if you prefer).

Honey to taste

1. Peel and slice the apple, place in a pan with the honey, cook slowly until tender
2. Follow the method for the Vegetable and Mince Pies

Day Three

Breakfast - muesli, skimmed or soya milk,
wholemeal toast or grain cookies
herbal or china tea.

Lunch - Cheese and onion pie, low fat
yoghurt, herbal or china tea.

Evening meal - Shepherds pie without potatoes, stir
fried vegetables, easy garlic or herb bread, apple pie,
herbal or china tea.

Both breakfast and lunch are easily taken care of, the
only preparation today is for your evening meal.

Shepherds pie without potatoes - pre heat oven 400f/200c gas mark 6

SHORT CUT use tinned lentils (without additives)

1 400g tin of lentils or soya mince
1 small onion peeled and chopped
2 sticks of celery scrubbed and chopped
1 table spoon of sunflower oil (if on a low fat diet, use
water instead of the oil)

1 teaspoon full of yeast extract or vegetable stock cube
1 clove of garlic - optional
8oz 240g peeled or scrubbed, then grated parsnips

1. Lightly cook the onion and celery, in sunflower oil (if on a low flat diet, cook them in a little water)
2. Grease an oven proof dish (with lid)
3. Add the lentils to the onion, mix and place them in the oven proof dish
4. Mix the yeast extract with a little water and add it to the lentils
5. Cover the top with grated parsnips
6. Cover with a lid and cook for approx 15-20 minutes

Easy Garlic Bread

1 oz 30g sunflower margarine
1 or 2 cloves of garlic chopped or pressed
2 slices of wholemeal bread

1. Place the margarine and garlic in a dish and mix together
2. Spread two slices of wholemeal bread with the margarine / garlic mixture

3. Place one slice of bread on top of the other (margarine sides facing in)
4. Wrap the bread in cooking foil
5. Place the bread in a hot oven for approx 3 minutes (until margarine has melted into the bread)

This method is quick and easy and there is no waste for the single person.

Slimmers should use a low fat spread.

Herb Bread

Pinch of mixed herbs
1 oz 30g sunflower margarine
2 slices of wholemeal bread

1. Follow the same method as for garlic bread

Maize Pudding

Follow the recipe for maize custard then add washed dried fruit to taste.

Day Four

Breakfast - chopped apple / natural low fat yoghurt, wholemeal toast, herbal or china tea.

Lunch - Cheese and biscuits, slice of carob cake, herbal or china tea.

Evening meal- vegetables and cashew nut stir fry, apricot crunch, maize custard.

Lunch

Cheese and biscuits - You can obtain a range of wholemeal crackers, rice cakes, water biscuits from supermarkets, check the labels. Slimmers should use low fat cheese spread or pate.

Evening Meal

Vegetable and Cashew Nut Stir Fry

1 oz 30g washed cashew nuts
1 tablespoon sunflower oil (slimmers omit the oil).
pinch of mixed herbs
2 oz 60g mushrooms - washed and chopped
2 radishes - cleaned and sliced

T'ai Chi Long Life Diet

2 cleaned and chopped sticks of celery
finely chopped broccoli
1 small onion peeled and finely chopped
2oz 60 g brown rice
1/2 pt water
soy sauce to taste

1. Bring the water to the boil in a pan
2. Add the brown rice
3. Turn the heat down, cover the pan with a lid and simmer for approximately 20 minutes (you may use a micro wave although it takes approximately 25 minutes; use a suitable container)
4. Add the oil to the wok, lightly cook the cashews until they are golden, then remove them from the wok. (Slimmers, do not use oil - dry roast the cashews instead)
5. Add the vegetables to the wok, cook until they achieve your preferred texture
6. Add the cooked rice, cashew nuts and herbs then flavour them with soy sauce to taste

Apricot Crunch - pre heat oven 400f/200c gas mark 6

3 oz 90g dried apricots (soak overnight in cold water)
Topping
2oz 60g sunflower margarine - slimmers use low fat margarine
2oz 60g oats
2oz 60g maize flour
1 tablespoon honey

1. Place the apricots in a pan and cover them with water, bring to the boil, lower the heat and simmer for 10 minutes
2. Prepare the topping by creaming the margarine and honey together
3. Add the oats, and maize, mix well
4. Grease a small oven proof dish
5. Add the apricots, cover them with the topping
6. Bake for approx. 10 minutes or until golden

An alternative is a recipe invented by my husband. For the topping, mix dried oats with honey (omitting the margarine). This is ideal if you wish to lose weight and provides an excellent topping for apples, bananas etc.

Day Five

Breakfast - wholemeal pancakes with honey topping, herbal or china tea

Lunch - wholemeal sandwich, grain cookie, herbal or china tea

Evening Meal - cauliflower cheese, rice, roast parsnips, carrots and peas; carob pudding, natural yoghurt, herbal or china tea

Breakfast

SHORT CUT
Pancakes are delicious with a sweet topping or filled with a savoury one. They are easy to make and once cold will keep in an air tight container until the following day (pancakes will freeze).

Pancakes
4oz 120g plain wholemeal flour or mixed flours
1 free range egg
1/4 pt skimmed or soya milk
Sunflower oil for cooking, slimmers use spray oil

1. Place all of the ingredients into a mixing bowl
2. Beat together with a fork until the mixture is runny and air bubbles form
3. Lightly grease a frying pan (a non stick frying pan is the easiest to use)
4. This part can be tricky so be careful, add 2 - 3 table spoons of the mixture to the frying pan, tilt the pan to allow the mixture to cover the base of the pan. Cook on medium heat until the pancake starts to set round the edges
5. If needed, add a little more oil, by lifting one corner of the pancake with a fish spatula
6. When the pancake starts to set in the middle, this is the time to turn it over. This can be done by using a spatula
7. When golden on both sides turn out onto a plate Top breakfast pancakes with honey

This mixture should make 4 - 5 pancakes depending on the size of your frying pan. Allow spare pancakes to cool and store in an air-tight container in the refridgerator.

Serving suggestion - savoury pancakes: fill with cooked mixed vegetables and cover with garlic mushrooms.

Evening meal

Cauliflower Cheese - pre heat oven 400f/200c gas mark 6

1/2 a cauliflower washed and cut into florets (cover the other half with cling film for use at a later date).
1 oz 30g maize flour
1/4 pt skimmed or soya milk
2oz cheese (grated)
soy sauce to season
1 clove of crushed garlic-optional
1 slice of wholemeal bread (grated)

1. Place the cauliflower in a pan and cover with enough water to boil, then simmer until the cauliflower is cooked (test with a fork)
2. Pour the milk into a pan and heat it gently
3. Mix the flour with a little cold milk and cream it into a smooth paste
4. Add the grated cheese, soya sauce and garlic, then turn up the heat and stir until the sauce thickens
5. Grease an oven proof dish
6. Drain the water from the cauliflower (note: the liquid can be saved and used for stock)

7. Place the cauliflower in a dish, cover with the cheese sauce, top with grated bread crumbs
8. Bake for approximately 15 minutes or until the bread crumbs are golden

Carrots

2 medium carrots scrubbed and cut into slices
1 teaspoon sunflower margarine (slimmers - lightly spray the foil and carrots with extra virgin olive oil)

1. Tear off a piece of cooking foil large enough to wrap and enclose the carrots
2. Place the carrots in the middle of the foil and top with margarine
3. Sprinkle a little parsley over the carrots
4. Wrap into a parcel and place on a baking tray
5. Bake in the oven for 20 -25 minutes

Rice

2oz 60g brown rice
1/2 pt water

1. Bring the water to the boil in a saucepan

2. Add the rice
3. Cover with a lid and simmer for approx 20 minutes
(if using microwave allow 25 minutes cooking time,
place in suitable container)

Peas - Fresh or frozen, place in saucepan, cover with
a little water and cook until tender

Day Six

Breakfast - popcorn, wholemeal toast, herbal or china tea.

Lunch - kidney bean and vegetable soup, wholemeal bread bap, fruit cake, herbal or china tea.

Evening Meal - lentil and tahini bake, vegetable stew, grain cookies, herbal tea.

Breakfast

Popcorn

1 table spoon sunflower oil
1 oz 30g popping corn
(Slimmers - use a pop corn maker as they do not require any oil).
CAUTION - do not remove the pan lid while the corn is popping. It is a good idea to use a clear glass lid so that you can view the process.

1. Heat the oil in a pan
2. Add the corn

3. Cover the pan with a lid
4. <u>When you hear the corn start to pop, hold the pan just above the heat</u>
5. <u>Caution</u> - Popcorn burns very easily. When the corn stops popping remove the pan from above the heat
6. Sweeten with honey or season with sea salt, or cover with skimmed or soya milk

Lunch

Kidney Bean and Vegetable Soup

Follow the recipe for easy cook vegetable soup (page 86), add one small can of washed and drained kidney beans.

Evening Meal

Lentil and Tahini Bake - pre heat oven 300f/150c gas mark 4

3oz red split lentils
1/2 pt water

1 onion peeled and chopped
1/2 teaspoon dried sage
1 tablespoon tahini
soy sauce to taste

1. Rinse and clean the lentils and remove any grit
2. Place the lentils and water into a large pan and bring to the boil (be careful that the water does not boil over)
3. Lower the heat and cook until all the water is absorbed
4. Add the rest of the ingredients, stir well
5. Grease an oven proof dish
6. Spoon in lentil mixture
7. Bake for approximately 25 minutes

Vegetable Stew

1 parsnip peeled and chopped
1 carrot scrubbed and sliced
1 onion peeled and chopped
1 leek cleaned and chopped
2 sticks celery cleaned and chopped
1 teaspoon of yeast extract
pinch of mixed herbs
1 table spoon maize flour

T'ai Chi Long Life Diet

1. Place all the ingredients (except the maize flour) into a pan and bring to the boil, lower the heat and simmer for approximately 15 minutes
2. Mix the maize flour with a little cold water to make a smooth paste
3. Add the maize flour paste to the stew, stir for 2 - 3 minutes, remove from the heat, season with sea salt, it is now ready to serve

Day Seven

Breakfast - French toast, herbal or china tea

Lunch - wholemeal sandwich, fruit and nuts, herbal or china tea

Evening Meal - mixed bean hot pot, easy garlic bread, herbal or china tea

Breakfast

French Toast

2 slices wholemeal bread
1 free range egg (beaten)
1 table spoon skimmed or soya milk
Sea salt to taste
Sunflower oil to shallow fry

1. Beat the egg, milk and salt together in mixing a bowl
2. Dip the bread into the egg mixture
3. Shallow fry on both sides until golden brown

Evening Meal

Mixed Bean Hot Pot - pre heat oven 400f/200c gas mark 6

For this recipe you will need 4oz 120g of cooked beans. If you are using dried beans, please remember that they must be soaked overnight then thoroughly boiled for at least 15 minutes (to kill off harmful enzymes etc.) until tender. Cooked beans will freeze, alternatively you can buy tinned cooked beans from most supermarkets.

1 carrot scrubbed and chopped
1 onion scrubbed and chopped
A little freshly grated ginger - optional
1 clove of crushed garlic - optional
1 mushroom scrubbed and chopped
Pinch of mixed herbs
1 tablespoon maize flour to thicken
1/4 pt vegetable stock

Soy sauce to taste

1. Grease an oven proof dish

2. Place the vegetables, cooked beans, and stock into the dish
3. Cover with a lid and place in the oven, allow to cook for approx 30 minutes until the vegetables are tender (add more stock if necessary)
4. Mix the maize flour to a smooth paste with a little cold water
5. Add to the beans and vegetables, stir well, at the same time add the herbs and season with soy sauce to taste. Return the hotpot to the oven for another 8 minutes

Soups

(Quantities are for four persons)

Barley Soup

(This soup is soothing to the stomach, although it is an acquired taste)

1oz 30g barley
1/2 pt vegetable stock
1/2 teaspoon mint
sea salt to taste

1. Stir the barley into the vegetable stock
2. Cook gently for 10 minutes
3. Remove from the heat, allow the soup to stand for approximately 15 minutes to allow barley to swell
4. Reheat the soup (eat very slowly)

Cauliflower Soup

1 medium size cauliflower
1 onion peeled and chopped
1 tablespoon chopped parsley
1 bay leaf
1 pt vegetable stock

1/2 pt soya or skimmed milk
Sea salt to taste

1. Clean and cut the cauliflower into florets
2. Put them into a large pan with all the other ingredients
3. Bring to the boil
4. Lower the heat, cover the pan with a lid
5. Cook for 30 minutes
6. Remove the bay leaf, liquidise and adjust the seasoning to taste

Lentil and Carrot Soup

2 tablespoons sunflower oil
2 onions peeled and chopped
1 lb carrots scrubbed chopped and cooked
1 3/4 pts stock
Pinch sage
Pinch parsley
Pinch thyme
8oz 240g cooked lentils
soy sauce to taste

1. Heat the oil in a pan and gently cook the onions
2. Place all ingredients into a blender and liquidise
3. Return the soup to a clean pan
4. Cook for approximately 15 minutes, stirring occasionally
5. Season to taste with soy sauce

Onion Soup with Cheese

1 lb 480g onions, peeled and sliced into fine rings
1 tablespoon sunflower oil
1 tablespoon mixed flours
1 1/2 pts vegetable stock
2 teaspoons yeast extract
4 oz 120g grated vegetarian cheese
4 slices of wholemeal bread
2 cloves garlic
sea salt to taste

1. Heat the oil in a large pan, add the onions, cook over low heat for 15 minutes (stirring occasionally)
2. Add the flour and allow to cook for 2 minutes
3. Mix the yeast extract with the stock, add the garlic and then add this mix to the onions. Bring to the boil stirring continuously until the soup thickens slightly

4. Lower the heat, cover the pan with a lid and simmer for 30 minutes
5. Before serving, toast the bread, break it into rough pieces and place in the bottom of the soup bowls Pour in the soup, top with grated cheese
6. Place under the grill to allow the cheese to melt

Butter Bean Soup

1 tin of butter beans
1 full bulb of garlic (although this may seem a lot, it tastes wonderful and is very beneficial if you are feeling under par)
1 pint vegetable stock
1 tea spoon of yeast extract or soy sauce to taste
Pinch of sage

1. Place the vegetable stock into a pan
2. Peel the garlic and add to the pan, bring to the boil then simmer for 15 minutes
3. Add the butter beans, heat thoroughly
4. Place the contents of the pan into a blender
5. Return the contents of the blender to the pan and gently reheat, adding the rest of the ingredients

Carrot and Ginger Soup

4 large carrots peeled and cut into chunks
1 leek, cleaned and sliced
2 inches of ginger root - diced
1 level teaspoon of sage
1 level teaspoon of thyme

1. Place all the ingredients into a large pan, cover
   with water (enough to well cover the vegetables)
   Bring to the boil and cook until the carrots are soft
2. Liquidise the soup until smooth

As an alternative, reduce the amount of carrots by half
and then add 1 mug of dried yellow split peas or red
lentils. Cook until the pulses are thoroughly cooked to
kill off any harmful enzymes etc. and are completely
soft, then liquidise.

Main Course Suggestions for the Whole Family (3 - 4 servings)

Vegetable Lasagne (without tomatoes) - pre heat oven 400f/200c gas mark 6

9 strips of ready to cook in the oven lasagne (wholemeal)
2 lb 960g grated carrots
1 large onion peeled and chopped
4 sticks celery scrubbed and chopped
1 clove garlic
1/4 pt vegetable stock

Cheese Sauce
4oz 120g grated vegetarian cheese
1oz 30g sunflower margarine
1/4 pt skimmed or soya milk
season with soy sauce
Wholemeal flour to thicken sauce

Topping
4 oz 120g grated vegetarian cheese

1. Bring 1/4pt of stock to the boil in a pan, add the celery and garlic, turn the heat down and simmer until tender
2. Cheese Sauce. Melt the margarine in a pan, add the

flour and mix together, turn the heat down low and cook for 2 - 3 minutes

3. Add the milk, turn the heat up stirring the sauce all the time until it starts to bubble. Turn the heat down and keep stirring until the sauce thickens, add the cheese and season with soy sauce to taste
4. Grease a lasagne dish
5. Cover the bottom of the dish with a little of the celery and stock
6. Cover with wholemeal lasagne.
7. Cover the lasagne with grated carrot and chopped onion.
8. Then cover with a layer of cheese sauce
9. Continue to build in layers
10. Sprinkle grated cheese on the top
11. Cook until golden brown

Spring Cabbage Lasagne

Follow the recipe above adding a layer of freshly cleaned spring cabbage to your ingredients. Cook in the same way.

Pizza - pre heat oven 400fh/200c, gas 6

You can buy wholemeal pizza bases from some health food shops. They generally come in packs of two.

Pizza Topping

3 large size carrots peeled and chopped
1/2 teaspoon dried sage
1/2 teaspoon dried thyme
1 clove of crushed garlic
Some finely chopped ginger
1 onion, halved and cut into thin slices
Chopped mushrooms
Sweetcorn
Grated cheese

1. Place the carrots, herbs, garlic and ginger into a pan and cover with water. Cook until the carrots are completely soft
2. Mash / liquidise carrots etc. until pureed
3. Lightly grease some tin-foil and place a pizza base onto the foil
4. Cover the base with a layer of the carrot puree, then cover with onions, mushrooms sweetcorn and then top with the grated cheese

5. Bake in the oven for approx 12-15 minutes

Stir Fry Wraps

1 Packet of wholemeal chapattis
1 Clove of garlic, crushed
1 inch of ginger root chopped
1 handful of very small broccoli florets
Some sliced radishes
1 Onion, chopped
some mushrooms – chopped
1 stick of celery - chopped
Soy sauce to taste
Honey to taste

1. Pre heat the oven as per the instructions on the packet of chapattis
2. Place the broccoli in a jug and cover with boiling water, leave for approx. 5 minutes
3. Heat a little oil in a wok or frying pan and add the garlic and ginger
4. Add the onion and celery
5. Add the broccoli, mushrooms and radishes
6. Add approximately 1 tablespoon of soy sauce and honey plus a little water. Adjust to taste
7. Cook for approx. 10 minutes

8. Cook the chapattis as per the instructions on the packet (do not over cook)

Place a chapatti on a plate and using a straining spoon, place a small pile of vegetables in the middle of the wrap. Roll the wrap up (repeat until the mixture and chapattis are used.

Savoury Rice with Leeks

8oz 240g leeks
2oz 60 g sunflower margarine
6oz 180g brown rice
1 pt vegetable stock
4oz 120g mushrooms scrubbed and chopped
3 tablespoons tahini
3oz 90g flaked almonds (toasted)

1. Remove the outside leaves from the leeks and cut off the roots
2. Wash them thoroughly
3. Cut the leeks in half from the top to the bottom
4. Cut into 1" pieces
5. Melt the margarine in a large pan (with lid)
6. Add the leeks and mushrooms, cook gently for 3

minutes (stirring occasionally)
7. Add the rice and fry for another 2 minutes
8. Stir in the stock and bring to the boil
9. Turn down the heat, cover the pan with a lid and simmer for 30 minutes (until the rice is cooked)
10. Stir in the tahini; sprinkle individual portions with almonds

Butter Bean And Parsnip Bake - pre heat oven 400f/200c gas mark 6

1 large can of butter beans
2 tablespoons sunflower oil
2 sticks celery scrubbed and chopped
2 carrots scrubbed and chopped
1/2 pt vegetable stock
4oz 120g dried mustard greens (available from Chinese supermarkets)

Topping
2lb cleaned and grated parsnips
2oz 60g oats
2oz 60g mixed fours
2 tablespoons sunflower oil

1. Grease a deep ovenproof dish

2. Heat the oil in a pan and gently fry the chopped vegetables
3. Cover the mustard greens with boiling water (to remove any preservatives). Then drain them and cut the greens into manageable pieces
4. Mix the beans, vegetables, mustard greens and stock together in greased dish
5. Place 3/4 of the grated parsnips on top of the bean mixture
6. Place the flour, oats and cooking oil in a mixing bowl and stir well
7. Mix the remaining parsnips with the flour mixture and pile on top of parsnips
8. Cook in the oven for approximately 20 - 25 minutes

Sweet Corn Flan - pre heat oven 400f/200c gas mark 6

4 oz 120g sweet corn
4 oz 120g vegetarian cheese
3 free range eggs
1 clove pressed or chopped garlic (optional)
Soy sauce to season

Pastry
4oz 120g self raising wholemeal flour
2oz 60 g sunflower margarine
Water to bind
1 tablespoon sesame seeds (optional)

1. Place the flour into a mixing bowl, add the margarine and rub together using your fingers, until it attains a bread crumb like texture
2. Bind together by adding a little cold water
3. Turn out onto a floured surface
4. Roll the mixture out with a rolling pin
5. Grease a flan dish
6. Line the flan dish with pastry
7. Add the sweet corn to the flan dish and spread evenly
8. Beat the eggs together, add a little soy sauce
9. Mix half the cheese with the eggs and pour over the sweetcorn
10. Sprinkle the rest of the cheese over the top of the flan
11. Bake in the oven for 25 - 30 minutes until the top is nice and golden and the mixture is set

Vegetable Stew With Bean Curd

1/2 lb white turnips cleaned and chopped
1 lb carrots scrubbed and chopped
1/2 lb onions peeled and chopped
1 clove garlic crushed or pressed - optional
1/2 pt vegetable stock
1/2 lb garden peas
1/4 lb mushrooms
2 tablespoons sunflower oil
1 teaspoon mixed herbs
Season with sea salt
1 tablespoon maize flour to thicken the stew
8oz bean curd (tofu)

1. Cut the bean curd into bite size cubes
2. Heat the cooking oil in a frying pan
3. Add the bean curd, cook for approximately 1 minute on each side (until golden)
4. Put a little soy sauce into a dish, put the bean curd into the dish and leave to soak (turning occasionally)
5. Put the left over oil into a large pan and add the vegetables (stir well)
6. Add the stock and bring to the boil, turn the heat down and simmer for 15 minutes

7. Mix the maize with a little cold water to form a smooth paste
8. Add to the stew, stirring all the time
9. Add the bean curd and soy sauce
10. Stir lightly
11. Ready to serve

Lentil Rissoles

8oz 240g red split lentils
1 pt water
2 tablespoons tahini
1 teaspoon sage
1 onion peeled and finely chopped
5 slices wholemeal bread grated
1-2 free-range eggs - beaten
Sunflower oil to shallow fry the rissoles
Add Soy sauce to taste

1. Remove any grit from the lentils
2. Bring the water to the boil in a large pan, add the lentils
3. Boil for ten minutes then reduce the heat (Beware of the water frothing and boiling over)
4. Allow the water to be absorbed into the lentils
5. Add the chopped onion, tahini and sage, mix well

6. Add some of the bread crumbs if needed to stiffen mixture
7. Form into rissole shapes, dip them into the beaten egg and then dip them into the bread crumbs
8. Shallow fry on both sides for approx 5 minutes

Cashew Nut and Mushroom Roast - pre heat oven 300f/150c gas mark 2

1 tablespoon sunflower oil
6oz 180g cashew nuts
1 small onion - finely chopped
2 cloves crushed garlic
1 teaspoon yeast extract
1/4 pt vegetable stock
1/2 teaspoon rosemary
1/2 teaspoon thyme
1 lb 480g scrubbed and grated carrots
1 free-range egg - beaten
1oz sunflower margarine
8oz 240g mushrooms
4oz 120g wholemeal bread crumbs

1. Heat the oil and gently fry the onions
2. Grind the cashew nuts in a nut mill or blender, mix the nuts with the bread crumbs

3. Add the beaten free range egg, to the nuts and bread crumb mix
4. Mix the grated carrots with the herbs, add the cooked onions and garlic, then add to nut mix
5. Mix the yeast extract with the stock, then add this to the other ingredients
6. Melt the margarine, lightly cook the mushrooms
7. Grease a loaf tin
8. Add half the nut mixture, pressing it well into the corners of the tin
9. Cover with the mushrooms
10. Add the remaining nut mixture
11. Cover with baking foil, bake for approx 1 hour
12. Leave to stand for ten minutes before turning out and serving

Mushroom Goulash

1 large onion - peeled and chopped
2oz 60g sunflower margarine
2 cloves of garlic - optional
1 lb mushrooms
Sea salt to taste
4 tablespoons vegetable stock
1/2 pt natural yoghurt

1 tablespoon of maize flour to thicken

1. Melt the margarine in a pan
2. Add the onions and cook gently for 5 minutes
3. Stir in the mushrooms and cook for a further 5 minutes
4. Add the stock then the seasoning, stir well
5. Cover the pan with a lid and cook on a low heat for approximately 10 minutes
6. Mix the yoghurt and flour together
7. Stir them into the other ingredients
8. Cook gently on low heat until heated through
9. Serve on a bed or rice, garnish with fresh parsley

Vegetable Yorkshire Pudding - pre heat oven 400fh/200c gas mark 6

4 oz 120 g plain wholemeal flour or gram flour
Pinch of sea salt - optional
1 free range egg (beaten)
1/2 pt skimmed or soya milk
1 tablespoon sunflower oil
Cooked mixed vegetables of your choice

1. Add the flour to the mixing bowl along with the

salt, then add the egg
2. Slowly add the milk - stirring with wooden spoon
3. Beat or whisk the mixture to add air (you should see air bubbles in the mixture). For best results allow the batter mixture to stand for 5-10 minutes
4. Grease a medium size Yorkshire pudding tin with oil and place it in the oven until the oil is hot
5. Spread the vegetables over the base of the tin
6. Pour the batter over the vegetables
7. When the batter has risen, lower the heat, and cook for a further 20-25 minutes until golden and thoroughly cooked

Stuffed Marrow - pre heat oven to 400f/200c gas mark 6

1 marrow
2 tablespoons sunflower oil
1 small onion - finely chopped
4oz 120g cooked millet
4oz 120g cashew nut pieces
4oz 120g mushrooms scrubbed and finely chopped
1 teaspoon dried parsley
1 teaspoon dried marjoram
Sea salt to taste

1. Cut off the ends of the marrow and scrub the skin clean, then cut the it in half (length ways) and scoop out the seeds
2. Heat the oil in a pan and cook the onions (just enough to soften them). Add the mushrooms, cook gently
3. Stir in the cooked millet, nuts, herbs and seasoning.
4. Divide the mixture in half
5. Fill each half of marrow halves side by side with the mixture
6. Grease an ovenproof dish, place the marrow in the dish and cover with foil
7. Cook for 45-50 minutes (until the marrow is tender)
8. For an alternative stuffing use cooked red split lentils mixed with grated cheese and seasoned with soy sauce

Meat Dishes

This section is for people who like to eat meat. The following recipes are acceptable, although meat should not be eaten more than twice a week.

Where possible buy free-range poultry.

Never cook poultry when it is frozen, frozen meat must be allowed to thaw at room temperature, or in the ordinary part of the refrigerator. Never plunge poultry into hot water to defrost.

T'ai Chi Long Life Diet

Always wash poultry well and remove the giblets.

Chicken with Apricots - pre heat oven 300f/150c gas mark 2

8oz 240g dried apricots - soaked overnight
2 tablespoons of honey
3 lb chicken

1. Wash the chicken thoroughly (both inside and out) with cold water
2. Stuff with 3/4 of the apricots (keep the liquid)
3. Place in a roasting tin, cover with cooking foil and cook in accordance with the sellers instructions until the juices run clear (remove the foil for the last 15 minutes)
4. Blend the honey, apricots plus liquid from the apricots together. Heat the mixture gently in a pan and serve with the cooked chicken

Chicken With Almonds

1oz 30g toasted flaked almonds
12oz 360g cooked chicken
1 small onion - peeled and chopped

8oz 240g sliced mushrooms
1oz 30g sunflower margarine
2 teaspoons corn flour
1/2 pt skimmed or soya milk
1/2 oz grated root ginger
Pinch of nutmeg
5oz 150g natural yoghurt
Yolks of 2 free-range eggs
Sea salt to taste

1. Heat the margerine in a pan, add onion and mush
   rooms, cook until they are a pale gold colour
2. Add the corn flour and stir well, allow to cook for
   2-3 minutes
3. Slowly stir in the milk, keep stirring until the milk
   comes to the boil
4. Add the chicken (previously cut into bite sized
   pieces), ginger and grated nutmeg
5. Cook for 5-6 minutes
6. Season to taste, pour out onto a serving dish
7. Garnish with flaked almonds and yoghurt

Chicken Breasts With Herbs and Vegetables

4 boneless chicken breasts

T'ai Chi Long Life Diet

Soy sauce to taste
Soya flour to coat
1oz 30g sunflower margarine
2 small white turnips cut into match-sticks
2 parsnips peeled and cut into match sticks
2 carrots peeled and cut into match sticks
1 handful of chopped parsley
1 teaspoon sorrel
1/2 pt stock
1/2 pt natural yoghurt

1. Rinse the chicken with cold water
2. Dust with soya flour
3. Melt half the margarine in a frying pan large enough to hold all of the chicken breasts
4. Cook the chicken on both sides until golden
5. Remove from the heat and leave to one side
6. Melt the remaining margarine in a large pan, add the vegetables and herbs
7. Add a little of the vegetable stock and cook for a few minutes
8. Add the chicken and the rest of the stock, and bring to the boil, then lower the heat and cook for 30 minutes

9. Remove the chicken breasts from the pan and place them on a serving dish
10. Blend the vegetables and stock in a blender, then return the contents to a clean pan
11. Stir in the yoghurt, slowly reheat the mixture, season with soy sauce
12. Spoon the mixture over the chicken breasts and serve

Turkey Loaf - pre heat oven 300f/150c gas mark 2

12oz 360g cooked turkey (slices or chunks)
4oz 120g wholemeal breadcrumbs
1 small onion peeled and chopped
4oz 120g mushrooms scrubbed and chopped
Handful fresh chopped parsley
1 large free-range egg (beaten)
Soy sauce to taste

1. Put the turkey, breadcrumbs, onion, mushrooms and parsley into a mixing bowl, mix well together
2. Stir in the beaten egg, season with soy sauce to taste
3. Grease a loaf tin
4. Transfer the mixture to the loaf tin

5. Press the mixture well down into the corners of the tin
6. Smooth the top level with a knife
7. Bake for 40 - 60 minutes, leave to stand for approximately ten minutes before turning out onto a serving dish

Fish

White fish may also be eaten, although again, no more than twice a week.

Grilled Cod

4 cutlets or cod steaks
1oz 30g sunflower margarine
1-2oz 30-60g grated cheese
1-2oz 30-60g fresh wholemeal bread crumbs
Sea salt to taste

1. Grease a grill pan
2. Wash the fish well with cold water
3. Place in the grill pan, grill quickly for 8 - 10 minutes
4. Remove from heat and stand to one side
5. Cream the cheese and margarine together in a mixing bowl and add the bread crumbs

6. Turn the fish over and spread with the cheese and bread crumbs mixture (on the uncooked side)
7. Cook on reduced heat for 5-6 minutes

Fish Cake - pre heat oven 400f/200c gas mark 5

1lb 480g cooked fish
1oz 30g sunflower margarine
8oz 240g grated parsnips
2 free range eggs
Sea salt to taste
Wholemeal breadcrumbs

1. Remove the skin and bones from the fish
2. Chop the fish - coarsely
3. Heat the margarine in a saucepan
4. Add the fish and one egg
5. Stir in the grated parsnips thoroughly
6. Season to taste
7. Grease a round tin or an oven proof dish
8. Press the mixture into the tin
9. Brush the top of the mixture with the beaten egg
10. Sprinkle wholemeal breadcrumbs on top of the fish

and parsnip mixture. Bake for approx 25 - 30 minutes

Savoury Haddock Casserole

1 lb 8oz 720g fillet of fresh haddock
2oz 60g sunflower margarine
2 level tablespoons wholemeal or maize flour
1/2 teaspoon sea salt
12oz 360g mushrooms - scrubbed and chopped
1 medium size onion - peeled and chopped
Soy sauce to taste
Fresh parsley to garnish

1. Rinse the fish under cold running water
2. Skin the fish and cut into 4 portions
3. Coat the fish with flour (lay both sides in the flour)
4. Melt 1oz 30g margarine in a frying pan
5. Fry the fish quickly on each side to seal in the juices (approx. 1 minute either side).
6. Grease an oven proof dish
7. Transfer the fish to an oven proof dish
8. Melt the remaining margarine in a frying pan, add the onion and mushrooms, cook gently
9. Add the vegetables to the fish, cover with a lid or cooking foil, bake for approx 30-40 minutes, garnish with fresh parsley, season to taste

Prawns With Rice

2 carrots - scrubbed and cut into match-sticks
1 large - onion peeled and finely chopped
8oz 240g peeled prawns
8oz 240g cooked brown rice
4oz 120g mushrooms - scrubbed and chopped
2 tablespoons sunflower oil
soy sauce to taste

1. Heat the oil in a wok
2. Lightly cook the prawns for 5 minutes
3. Remove the prawns from the wok
4. Add the vegetables, stir well, cover the wok with a lid, cook for approx 5 minutes, stirring occasionally
5. Add the brown rice, heat thoroughly
6. Add the prawns to the rice and vegetables, season to taste

Prawn and Corn Chowder

1 large onion - peeled and finely chopped
1/2oz 15g sunflower margarine
1lb 480g grated parsnips
Sea salt to taste
6oz 180g peeled prawns

7oz 210g sweet corn kernels
1 pt skimmed or soya milk
1/4 pt stock
3oz 90g grated vegetarian cheese

1. Melt the margarine in a large pan
2. Add the chopped onion and cook gently until soft
3. Add the grated parsnips and stock to the pan, bring to the boil
4. Turn the heat down and simmer for approximately 10 minutes (cover the pan with a lid)
5. Add the prawns and sweetcorn, stir well
6. Add the milk, stir well
7. Reheat, remove from the heat and stir in the grated cheese, Season to taste

Lunch Ideas

Vegetable Pate - pre heat oven 400f/200c gas mark 6

1 small onion - peeled and finely chopped
2 sticks celery - scrubbed and finely chopped
1 carrot - scrubbed and finely chopped
1 clove crushed garlic

1 tablespoon sunflower oil
4oz 120g ground cashew nuts
Pinch rosemary
Pinch thyme
1 tablespoon soy sauce
1 free range egg

1. Heat the oil in a pan
2. Add the onion, celery, carrot and garlic, cook gently for 3 minutes, stirring occasionally
3. Add the remaining ingredients and mix them in the pan
4. Place the mixture in a blender and liquidise until smooth
5. Grease a small oven proof dish, spoon in the mixture, smooth the top level with a knife
6. Cover with a lid or cooking foil, bake for 35 - 40 minutes, the pate should be firm to the touch.
7. Allow to cool before turning out

Quick Sandwich Spread

Lightly roasted nuts or seeds of your choice
A little water

1. Blend nuts or seeds of your choice with a little

water to make a spreading consistency

Left Over Vegetables

These make an excellent sandwich filling, simply mix together and season to taste with either soy sauce or sea salt.

Cheese Straws - pre heat oven 400f/200c gas mark 6

8oz 240g wholemeal flour
4oz 120g sunflower margarine
4oz 120g grated vegetarian cheese
2 tablespoons sesame seeds
Water to mix

1. Place the flour and margarine in a mixing bowl, rub the margarine into the flour with your fingers
2. Add the grated cheese, mix well
3. Add a little cold water to form a dough
4. Pull off small pieces of dough about the size of a tablespoon
5. Roll between the palms to form thick sticks 6" approximately long
6. Grease a baking tray, brush the tops of the cheese

straws with a little milk

7. Sprinkle with sesame seeds, bake in the oven for approximately 10 -15 minutes

Walnut Balls - pre heat oven 400f/200c gas mark 6

Level teaspoon of margarine
6oz 180g ground walnuts
4oz 120 g mushrooms - scrubbed and finely chopped
3oz 90g wholemeal bread crumbs
4oz 120g vegetarian cheese
1 onion - peeled and chopped
2 tablespoons parsley
1 free-range egg (beaten)
Sea salt

1. Melt the margarine in a pan, gently cook the mushrooms and onions for approximately 3 minutes
2. Mix all the dry ingredients together in a mixing bowl
3. Add the beaten egg and season to taste
4. Grease a baking tray
5. Shape the mixture into balls, bake in the oven for approximately 20 - 25 minutes until golden brown

Salads

Apricot Salad
4oz 120 g dried apricots - scalded and dried
1 small cauliflower - cleaned and cut into florets
4 oz 120g cooked peas
2oz 60g chopped walnuts (dry cook the walnuts in a pan for 2 minutes. Note: uncooked nuts are difficult to digest)
Fresh apple juice
Lettuce - cleaned and shredded
Sea salt to taste
Watercress for garnishing

1. Toss the lettuce in fresh apple juice
2. Line a serving dish with a bed of lettuce
3. Mix the rest of the ingredients together in a mixing bowl
4. Transfer the ingredients onto the bed of lettuce
5. Garnish with watercress

Almond Salad
2 bananas (although bananas are tropical fruit they do not contain a lot of acid so they may be eaten in moderation).

2oz 60g raisins
4oz 120g toasted almonds
1 carrot - scrubbed and finely grated
Mayonnaise to taste (see mayonnaise recipe)
Sea salt to taste
Fresh parsley to garnish

1. Mix the bananas, raisins, nuts and carrots in a bowl
2. Add the mayonnaise to taste
3. Garnish with chopped parsley

Nut and Vegetable Rice Salad

8oz 240g cooked brown rice
4oz 120g red cabbage - cleaned and finely chopped
1 carrot - scrubbed and grated
2oz 60g sultanas - (scalded)
2oz cashew nut pieces
1/4 pt tahini and apple dressing (see page 149)
1 tablespoon sunflower oil

1. Heat the oil in a pan
2. Add the cashew nuts, cook until golden
3. Mix the rice, fruit, vegetables and nuts in a salad
   bowl, pour the dressing over the salad and mix well

Tahini And Apple Dressing
3 tablespoons of tahini
2 teaspoons fresh apple juice
1/2 teaspoon yeast extract
1 clove crushed garlic
1 small finely chopped onion
sea salt to taste
5fl oz water

1. Put all the ingredients into a blender, liquidize until smooth

Mayonnaise
1 free-range egg
sea salt to taste
1/4 pt sunflower oil

2. Mix the first two ingredients together
3. Put them in a blender
4. Slowly add the oil to the blender, cover and blend in stages

Garlic Mayonnaise - the same as mayonnaise except add two cloves of crushed garlic.

Cakes And Puddings

No sugar is used in any of the recipes in this section. I have used honey as a sweetener.

Fruit Cake - pre heat oven 300/150c gas mark 2

6oz 180g wholemeal self raising flour
2oz 60g soya flour
3oz 90g ground almonds
8oz 240g sunflower margarine
1 lb 480g raisins
4oz 120g currants
4oz 120g sultanas
2 free-range eggs (beaten)
8oz 240g honey

1. Line an 8" cake tin with grease proof paper and grease well. Also tie grease proof paper round outer edge of tin. This stops the cake from cooking too quickly and avoids the outer edges burning and the middle of the cake from being undercooked
2. Cream the margarine and honey together in a bowl
3. Add the beaten eggs and flour, mix well
4. Mix in the fruit and ground almonds
5. Transfer the cake mixture into the tin

6. Place a piece of grease proof paper over the top of the tin to prevent the cake from burning
7. Bake in the oven for 1 - 1 1/2 hours
8. Test to see if cooked by inserting a skewer into the centre of the cake, it should come out clean

Icing

4oz 120g coconut cream
2 tablespoons boiling water

1. Grate the coconut cream, add boiling water and stir until creamy. Smooth over the cake and leave to set

Carrot Cake - pre heat oven 400f/200c gas mark 6

1 lb 480g plain wholemeal flour
1 teaspoon of cinnamon
1 teaspoon of nutmeg
1 tablespoon baking powder
8oz 240g sunflower margarine
8oz 240g honey
1lb 480g peeled and grated carrots

1. Mix the flour, cinnamon, nutmeg and baking powder in a mixing bowl

2. Put the margarine and honey in a saucepan (melt them together but do not allow them to burn)
3. Stir the melted margarine and honey mixture into a mixing bowl, with the dry ingredients
4. Stir in the grated carrot (thoroughly mix the carrots into the mixture)
5. If the mixture is too stiff, you may add a little cold water
6. Place the mixture into a greased loaf tin
7. Push the mixture right into the corners of the tin with the back of a spoon
8. Bake in the oven for approximately 70 - 80 minutes
9. The cake should be firm to the touch and when a skewer is inserted into the middle, it should come out clean
10. Allow the cake to cool in the tin before turning out (slide a knife gently all the way round the edge of the tin to help ease the cake out)

Flapjacks - pre heat oven 400f/200c gas mark 6

4oz 120 g sunflower margarine
4oz 120g honey
8oz 240g oats

1. Melt the margarine and honey in a pan, stir in the oats
2. Grease a shallow square cake tin
3. Transfer the mixture to the tin and level the surface with a knife
4. Bake for approx 20 -25 minutes
5. Mark into squares while still hot
6. Remove the flapjacks from tin when cold
7. For special occasions melt a carob bar and spread over the flapjacks

Wholemeal Scones - pre heat oven 400f/200c gas mark 6

2oz 60g sunflower margarine
8oz 240g self raising wholemeal flour
2oz 60g honey
4oz 120g sultanas
1 egg beaten plus enough milk to make 1/4 pt

1. Place the margarine and flour into mixing a bowl
2. Rub the margarine into the flour, add the sultanas and mix together
3. Mix the honey, egg and milk together
4. Pour nearly all the liquid into the mixing bowl, save

some to glaze the tops of the scones
5. Stir the liquid into the dry mixture (to form a dough)
6. Grease a baking sheet, flour a work surface and cut the dough into scone shapes with a pastry cutter
7. Glaze the tops of the scones with some of the liquid, bake for approximately 15 - 20 minutes

Beryl's Clootie Dumpling

1lb 480g wholemeal self raising flour
1 cup vegetable suet
1 cup honey
8oz 240g currents
8oz 240g raisins
8oz 240g sultanas
1 teaspoon ginger
1 teaspoon cinnamon
1 large cooking apple - peeled and grated

1. Place all the ingredients into a large mixing bowl
2. Mix together with cold water to form a soft 'dough like' pastry
3. Put the pudding into a damp pudding cloth which has been dusted with flour
4. Place the pudding in a large pan of boiling water

5. Note, the pudding should be 3/4 covered with water
6. Keep the water boiling, topping it up with boiled water from the kettle
7. Boil the pudding for 4 hours

Peach Upside Down Cake - pre heat oven 350fh/150c, gas mark 2

8oz 240g dried peaches - soaked overnight
6oz 180g sunflower margarine
4oz 120g honey
2 free-range eggs (beaten)
6oz 180g wholemeal self raising flour
A little skimmed or soya milk

1. Grease and line an 8" round cake tin
2. Arrange the peaches in the bottom of the tin
3. Put the margarine and honey into a mixing bowl
4. Cream together
5. Carefully mix in the flour and the eggs
6. Add a little milk if needed to form a dropping consistency
7. Spread the mixture carefully over the peaches
8. Bake for approximately 1 hour until it is firm to the touch

9. Allow to stand for a minimum of five minutes

Apple Cake - pre heat oven 360fh/180c, gas mark 4

5oz 150g wholemeal self raising flour
1/2 teaspoon mixed spice
3oz 90g honey
3oz 90g margarine
4oz 120g sultanas
6oz 180g diced apples
2 eggs (beaten)

1. Mix the flour and spices together
2. Rub in the margarine
3. Stir in the sultanas, apples and honey
4. Mix together with the beaten eggs
5. Grease a loaf tin and pour in the mixture
6. Bake for approx 30 – 40 minutes

All-bran Loaf - pre heated oven 360fh/180c, gas mark 4

1 mug of all-bran
1 mug sultanas
2/3 mug of honey

T'ai Chi Long Life Diet

1 mug of skimmed or soya milk
1 mug of wholemeal self raising flour
optional – grated root ginger, mixed spice

1. Put the All-bran, sultanas, honey and milk into a
   bowl, cover and leave to soak overnight
2. Grease a loaf tin and place a piece of greased foil
   or paper in the bottom of the tin
3. Pre heat the oven to 180 degrees or gas mark 4
4. Fold the flour into the mixture and mix well
5. Place mixture into the lightly greased tin and cook
   for approximately 1 hour

Bread - 400f/200c gas mark 5
1 dessertspoon honey
1oz 30g fresh yeast
1 1/4 pts warm water
2 1/2 lb 1200g plain wholemeal flour
2 tablespoons sunflower oil

1. Cream the honey and yeast together with a fork,
   until there are no lumps
2. Add 1/2 pt of warm water to the yeast
3. Cover with a clean cloth and stand in warm a place
   for 10 - 15 minutes (until the mixture starts to

froth and bubble)
4. When the yeast mixture is ready, beat the oil into it with a fork
5. Sieve the flour into a mixing bowl
6. Pour the yeast mixture onto the flour, add the remainder of the warm water by the cupful. (Note, you may not require all of the water)
7. Mix together until the dough forms
8. Turn the dough out onto a floured work surface
9. Kneed for about 10 minutes (the dough should feel smoother and more elastic)
10. Place the dough into a clean mixing bowl, cover with a cloth and stand it in a warm place, until it doubles in size (1 hour approximately)
11. Turn the dough out onto a floured work surface and knead it again for a few minutes
12. Divide the dough into two equal parts and shape them into smooth loaves
13. Put the loaves into two greased loaf tins
14. Cover with a cloth and leave them in a warm place until the dough reaches the top of the tins
15. Bake them in an oven for 10 minutes then turn the heat down to 300f/150c gas mark 2, for 30-40 minutes. To test when the loaf is cooked, tap it on the bottom with your knuckle, it should sound hollow

Electric breadmakers are also an excellent way of making your own bread, in addition they take all the effort out of it. I personally would not be without mine and find that I am able to eat freshly baked wholemeal bread every day. I suggest you follow the recipe guide for wholemeal bread which comes with your breadmaker's instructions, substituting sugar with honey.

Your bread maker will also make pizza bases and cakes.

Wheat Free Diet

In our modern times, more and more people are finding that they simply cannot tolerate wheat. The side effects of eating wheat can be quite devastating, ranging from volatile emotions to stomach disorders.

If you are unable to eat wheat it is a good idea to keep a packet of sugar free cornflakes in the cupboard. If you find you are hungry and do not have time to cook, try a dish of cornflakes with soya milk.

It is also possible to buy pasta made from corn or buckwheat at your local health food store.

Listed below are a few recipes to help get you started,

although I am sure that with practise, you will be able to add many more of your own.

The recipes in this section have kindly been donated by Sheena Judge and her mother - Beryl.

Wheat Free Bread - pre heat oven 400fh/200c, gas mark 5

1lb (480g) mixed flours – 8 oz barley, 5oz rye, 3 oz rice
1 sachet fast acting yeast
1 dessert spoon margarine
Warm water to mix

1. Place the flour, margarine and yeast into a warm basin (pre warm the basin in a warm oven or with hot water from the kettle, before starting)
2. Attach the dough hook to the mixer
3. Add the water [which is slightly warmer than tepid] (non wheat flour needs more water than wheat otherwise the mixture is too crumbly to work with). The correct consistency is a tacky texture when cut with a knife
4. Put some flour on a baking board or work surface and knead until your dough changes texture, this usually takes only a minute or two. If it crumbles

apart you need to add more water
5. Grease a 1lb loaf tin
6. Place the mixture into a tin and use your knuckles to spread the dough into the corners of the tin
7. Leave bread to rise above the top of the tin by placing it in an airing cupboard or warm room

IF THE BREAD DOESN'T RISE, THERE IS EITHER NOT ENOUGH WATER OR THE ROOM IS TOO COLD.

IF BREAD IS TOO HEAVY, USE LESS BUCK-WHEAT AND RYE FLOUR.

8. Bake in a pre heated oven for approximately 45 minutes
9. To test when the loaf is cooked, tap it on the bottom with your knuckles - it should sound hollow
10. Place the loaf on a baking rack to cool

The texture of this bread will be more crumbly than ordinary bread. For toast, place it under the grill, not in a toaster.

Wheat Free Pastry

1lb (480) mixed flours (rice, barley, rye, maize, soya)
1/2lb 240g margarine
Cold water. Note: non wheat flour needs more water, otherwise the pastry will crumble.

1. Place the flour and margarine in a mixing bowl
2. Mix with your hands until it forms a bread crumb consistency
3. Mix with cold water to bind the mixture together
4. Roll out onto a floured board

You may adjust the above quantities to match your needs, and make fruit pies and savoury pies from this recipe. When cooked, this pastry will freeze, enabling you to prepare your pies in advance.

Franzie Pan - pre heat oven 400fh/200c, gas 6

4oz 120g margarine
4oz 120g honey
4oz 120g ground almonds
1oz 30g flour
2 eggs
Sugar free jam and wheat free pastry to line one tart tin

1. Mix all the ingredients together except the jam and pastry (This forms the franzie pan mixture)
2. Line a greased dish with the pastry
3. Spread the sugar free jam (available from health food shops) on top of the pastry
4. Spread the franzie pan mixture over the top of the pastry
5. Bake for approx 35 – 40 minutes

Fruit Cake - pre heat oven 250fh/120c, gas 1/2
9oz 270g honey
9oz 270g margarine
9oz 270g mixed flours
2 teaspoons baking powder
1 teaspoon mixed spice
1lb 480g mixed fruit (cleaned, boiled and cooled)
5 eggs (beaten)

1. Grease and line a cake tin with grease proof paper
2. Mixed everything together, beat until smooth, pour into the lined cake tin
3. Bake for 2 hours at 120 degrees

Mixed Spice Buns - pre heat over 400fh/200c, gas mark 6

1lb (480g) mixed flours
2 teaspoons baking powder
8oz (240g) margarine
7oz (210g) honey
2 eggs (beaten) keep some of the egg mixture for brushing onto the buns
teaspoon mixed spice
8oz (240g) currants (boiled and cooled)

1. Mix all the ingredients together, form into ball shapes (approx the size of a golf ball)
2. Place on greased baking trays
3. Brush with the beaten egg
4. Bake at 400 degrees for approximately 12 minutes

Rock Buns - pre heat over 300fh/150c, gas mark 2

1lb (480g) mixed flours
2 teaspoons baking powder
1 teaspoon mixed spice
8oz (240g) honey
3 eggs (beaten)
1/2 lb (240g) mixed fruit (cleaned, boiled and cooled)

8oz (240g) margarine

1. Mix all the ingredients together
2. Shape into rounds with two dessertspoons i.e. use one spoon to scoop up a heaped spoonful of the mixture, and then use the second spoon to smooth and shape the top of the mixture into an egg shape or ball shape
3. Place the bun on a greased baking tray
4. Bake for approx 15 minutes

Questions and Answers About The Diet

Q   Surely eating fresh fruit is good for you?

A   Fruit contains many vitamins, it is true, but fruit also contains acid. Scientific research has shown that acid can add to the cause of illness such as arthritis. The same vitamins can be obtained from dried fruit without the acid.

Q   I have eaten potatoes for years, why can't you eat them on this diet?

A   Potatoes, tomatoes and aubergines are all part of the deadly nightshade family and although many people have eaten them for years, research is now finding that people who suffer from certain illnesses feel an improvement when they cut out these foods. This knowledge was made available to us in the late 1930s, scientific research is slowly providing evidence to back up that which was taught 3000 years ago.

Q   Am I guaranteed good health if I follow this diet?

T'ai Chi Long Life Diet

A   Not so many years ago, the Masters of times past would have answered yes. Because of the world we live in, it becomes more and more difficult to find foods without preservatives, we only have to look at the pollution around us.
This diet will certainly help improve the quality of your life, if followed properly.

Q   Do I have to follow this diet to benefit from practising LFA T'ai Chi?

A   The choice is a personal one, many people gain great benefit from practising LFA T'ai Chi while eating a typical Western diet.

Q   What can I gain by following this diet?

A   In the West we tend to accept aches and pains as part of the ageing process. WHY? I personally feel it is the quality of life which counts and that is why I follow this 3000 year old diet. If you wish to join me, you are very welcome.

Q   I am allergic to dairy products, can I follow this diet?

A   Because of your allergy you will have learnt to adapt your eating patterns. It's a fairly simple matter to adapt this diet to suit your needs.

If you are truly interested in good health, this diet should be practised together with the rest of our Arts. For further information on the LFA Health Arts, please send an A4 stamped addressed envelope to Stairway Distribution Limited, PO Box 19, Hedon, Hull, HU12 8YR, or visit our website www.leefamilyarts.com

T'ai Chi Long Life Diet

Information on Major Nutrients (the following information has been taken from various sources and offers and insight into different nutritional value of foods, please check the accuracy on the packets of products which you purchase).

Bean Curd (Tofu) per 100g serving

120mg potassium	500mg calcium
290kj energy	120mg phosphorus
7g protein	2.4mg iron
4g fat	0.7mg zinc
1g carbohydrate	5mg sodium

This is an excellent food for people on a low fat diet, however bean curd has no taste of its own and needs to be flavoured e.g. with soya sauce.

Lentils per 200g (cooked)

9g dietary fibre	40mg calcium
15g protein	50mg magnesium
1g fat	4.8mg iron
3.4g carbohydrate	2mg zinc
30mg sodium	0.2mg thiamine
420mg potassium	150mg phosphorus

Lentils are also excellent for people on a low fat diet, providing a valuable source of vegetable protein.

Red Kidney Beans per 75g serving

105mg calcium	310mg phosphorus
17g protein	135mg magnesium
1g fat	5mg iron
34g carbohydrate	2.1mg zinc
40mg sodium	0.41mg thiamine
870mg potassium	0.15mg Riboflavin
19g dietary fibre	

Kidney beans are an excellent source of vegetable protein and fibre.

Chickpeas per 75g serving

110mg calcium	225mg phosphorus
15g protein	120mg magnesium
5g fat	48mg iron
38g carbohydrate	1.8mg zinc
30mg sodium	0.35mg thiamine
600mg potassium	0.1mg riboflavin
11g dietary fibre	

Chickpeas are an excellent source of vegetable protein and fibre.

Lima Beans (Butter Beans) per 190g cooked

9.5g dietary fibre   165mg phosphorus
13g protein   6.5mg magnesium
1g fat   3.2mg iron
32g carbohydrate   1.9mg zinc
30mg sodium   0.25mg thiamine
760mg potassium

Butterbeans are an excellent source of vegetable protein and fibre.

Cashew Nuts per 30g serving

80mg magnesium   1mg iron
5g protein   0.1mg Thiamine
14g fat   8g carbohydrate

Cashew nuts have a high oil content of which 74 percent is unsaturated.

Soya Flour per 20g

1.5mg iron   48mg magnesium
7g protein   1mg zinc
5g fat   40mg calcium
5g carbohydrate   0.15mg thiamine
2.5g dietary fibre   330mg potassium

Soya flour contains a rich source of protein.

Rice Flour per 20g
25mg potassium
0.64g protein
8g carbohydrate
Rice flour contains a concentrated level of starch.

Wholemeal Flour per 100g

11g protein	8.7g fibre
2.1g fat	0.5g sodium
58.3g carbohydrate	

Millet per 40g

2.5mg iron	0.15mg thiamine
2g protein	1g fat
30g carbohydrate	4g dietary fibre
Calcium	

Millet is excellent for people who suffer from back problems and other joint related illnesses.

Brown Rice per 75g

6g protein	2.6g fat
55g carbohydrate	1.4g fibre

T'ai Chi Long Life Diet

Couscous per 63g
7.8g protein   44.8g carbohydrate
1.2g fat   3.6g fibre

Wholewheat Lasagne per 100g
13.4g protein   2.5g fat
66.2g carbohydrate

Wholemeal Bread per 50g
160mg potassium   6g protein
1.4mg iron   2g fat
3.2mg magnesium   23g carbohydrate
0.8mg zinc   4g dietry fibre
0.15mg thiamine   280mg sodium
0.05mg riboflavin

Dried Apricots per 25g
17g carbohydrate   6g dietary fibre
220mg vitamin A   2mg vitamin C
1.1mg iron

Dried apricots provide all the vitamins of fresh fruit without the acid. Please make sure that you scald all dried fruit before use to remove any preservatives.

Dried Currants per 10g
5g carbohydrate   5g fibre
30mg magnesium

Dried Dates per 33g
19mg magnesium   0.1mg iron
1g protein   21g carbohydrate
3g dietary fibre

Dried Figs per 30g
90mg calcium   30mg magnesium
20g carbohydrate   10g dietary fibre
0.5mg iron

Dried Raisins per 20g

13g carbohydrate   2g dietary fibre

Sultanas per 10g
6g carbohydrate   3g dietary fibre
1mg vitamin E

Honey per 15g
0.1g protein   11g carbohydrate
Nil fat

T'ai Chi Long Life Diet

Sugar Free Jam per 100g

0.4 protein
56g carbohydrate
0.1g fat

2.1g fibre
less than 0.1g sodium

Mushrooms (cultivated) per 50g

1g protein
84mg phosphorus

1g dietary fibre
0.2mg riboflavin

Chicken per 100g

170mg phosphorus
26g protein
14g fat
128mg cholesterol

22mg magnesium
1mg iron
1.6mg zinc
0.2mg riboflavin

Egg

109mg phosphorus
1.2mg iron
80mg vitamin A
0.15mg riboflavin

6g protein
5g fat
250mg cholesterol

Broccoli per 60g (cooked)

0.6mg iron
46mg calcium
1mg vitamin E
34mg vitamin C

1g carbohydrate
5g dietary fibre
250mg vitamin A

Cabbage per 50g (cooked)
3g carbohydrate   24mg vitamin C
Vitamin A variable

Carrots per 60g
5g carbohydrate   2g dietary fibre
765mg vitamin A   3mg vitamin C

Cauliflower per 60g (cooked)
0.4mg iron   30mg vitamin C
3g carbohydrate   2g dietary fibre

Onions per 40g (cooked)
2g carbohydrate   4mg vitamin C

Parsnip per 60g (cooked)
2g dietary fibre   5mg vitamin C
9g carbohydrate   1mg vitamin E

YOU MUST READ THIS SECTION

The LFA T'ai Chi Chang Ming diet book contains valuable information (and recipes) laid down over 3000 years ago, to help you to improve the quality of your life and promote good health. The diet allows the body's natural healing and rejuvenating powers to work. This book also draws together the whole spectrum of the Lee Family Arts.

The essence of the diet is to omit (or at least reduce) the intake of certain staple foods (potatoes, aubergines, tomatoes and peppers) of which the first three are known to belong to the Deadly Nightshade group of plants.

A percentage of the population are not adversely affected by these toxins.

Another percentage of the population have an immune system and / or a Chi energy system which can lock off the poisons and store them in the fat layers and tissues. This means that they become an accumulative poison which ultimately becomes active when the Chi energy system and / or the immune system fails by being overloaded, and is therefore unable to keep the poisons locked off. This results in the the individual contracting the horrendous and possibly incurable 20th century diseases.

The remaining percentage of the population are adversely affected by the poisons and are therefore always feeling under par or ill and cannot understand why. They are the ones diagnosed as not responding to treatment and because the source of the poison is not removed (i.e. the food they are eating), they will possibly never get well or do the things which healthy people do.

By following the principles in the Chang Ming Long Life Diet and Recipe Book, the body's immune system is given a boost because it is not having to waste energy fighting the poisons in the daily intake of food. This means that it gains the power to fight life threatening diseases. In addition, by practicing the LFA T'ai Chi Form, Dance, Stick, Silk, Sword, Nunchaku and Fan sets plus our K'ai Men (Taoist Yoga) and Breathing exercises, you can restore your natural energy levels and live a healthy life.

T'ai Chi Long Life Diet

Index -General

Index -General

T'ai Chi Long Life Diet

Index -Health Remedies and First Aid

Index -Health Remedies and First Aid

Index -Recipes

Index -Recipes

Index -Recipes

Index -Recipes

T'ai Chi Long Life Diet

CHANG MING

T'ai Chi Long Life Diet

CHANG MING

T'ai Chi Long Life Diet

CHANG MING

T'ai Chi Long Life Diet

193

CHANG MING

T'ai Chi Long Life Diet

CHANG MING